W9-DFL-795

W9-DFL-795

UNITED STATES AIR FORCE
TACTICAL AIR COMMAND

UNITED STATES AIR FORCE
TACTICAL AIR COMMAND

MICHAEL ROBERTS

Brian Trodd Publishing House Limited

Published in 1990 by
Brian Trodd Publishing House Limited
27 Swinton Street, London WC1X 9NW

Copyright © 1990 Brian Trodd
Publishing House Limited

All rights reserved. No part of this
publication may be reproduced, stored
in a retrieval system, or transmitted, in
any form or by any means, electronic,
mechanical, photocopying, recording or
otherwise, without permission in writing
from the publisher.

ISBN 1 85361 174 3

Typeset by August Filmsetting,
England

Printed in Portugal

Photographic acknowledgments

All photographs supplied by BTPH with
the exception of the following:
Boeing 29, 39, 40/41, 47 top & bottom;
Cessna 80 top; Hugh W. Cowin 42/43, 43:
Fairchild Republic 14/15, 64, 65 bottom;
General Dynamics 16, 23 top, 26, 32, 60
top, 60/61, 61 top, 75, 76 top & bottom;
Grumman 33, 50/51; Lockheed 68, 77;
McDonnell Douglas 13, 18/19, 22, 27 top,
30 bottom, 37; Northrop 54 inset bottom,
54/55, 55 inset bottom, 87; Raytheon
94/95; USAF endpapers, 1, 2/3, 4/5, 6, 15,
17, 20/21, 24 bottom, 34/35, 38 left, 50
inset, 52 left & right, 53 top left & right, 55
inset top, 57 top left, top right & bottom,
58 top, center & bottom, 58/59, 60 bottom,
61 bottom, 62, 63 top & bottom, 67, 72 top,
bottom left and bottom right, 73, 74
bottom, 78 top & bottom, 79 top & bottom,
81, 86/87, 88, 93; Westinghouse 24 top.
TRH Pictures: 7, 90; Hughes 92, 97 top;
Alan Landau 74 top; Lockheed 82/83;
McDonnell Douglas 25, 91 Rockwell 98/99;
USAF 8 left, 9 top, 11 top, 12 top, 23
bottom, 27 bottom, 30 top, 31, 36, 38 right,
49, 53 center left, 56, 65 top, 69 top, 83 top
& bottom, 84/85 top, 89, 96, 97 bottom, 99
inset.

Endpapers: Impressive in their shark
mouth markings is this line-up of 469th
TFS F-4Es
Page 1: An F-15 pilot's eye view of a
rendezvous with a KC-135A tanker
Title spread: Looking more like the
product of a Sci-Fi filmmaker's art than
a tactical fighter, Lockheed's F-117A
employs stealth technology to strike at
well-defended targets with pinpoint
accuracy
Right: A United Kingdom-based F-111
seen at optimum economic cruise
altitude as it returns from temporary
assignment in Turkey

Contents

"TAC is charged with organizing, equipping, training, administrating, and operating assigned or attached forces to ensure combat-ready forces capable of conducting worldwide tactical air operations. As the air component of the United States Readiness Command (USREDCOM), US Central Command (USCC), US Atlantic Command (LANTCOM), and US Southern Command (SOUTHCOM), TAC conducts, controls, and coordinates tactical air operations according to tasks assigned by those Commands. TAC is ready on a moment's notice to deploy powerful, tailored packages of airpower nonstop to any spot on the globe for support of the national interests. Support of the US Army is a vital responsibility of TAC. It has a versatile array of aircraft, ranging from supersonic jets to propeller-driven light aircraft, for conducting its missions of air defense, air superiority, close air support, interdiction, and counterair reconnaissance. TAC trains personnel for the tactical air forces overseas and supervises the training of a large percentage of Air National Guard and Air Force Reserve flying squadrons."

TAC Mission Statement

Introduction

Tactical Air Command's mission is "to organize, train, equip, and maintain combat-ready forces capable of rapid deployment and employment and to ensure that strategic air defense forces are ready to meet the challenges of peacetime air sovereignty and wartime defense."

The Command is one of the world's largest air forces in its own right, and with the units it would gain in wartime from the Air National Guard (ANG) and the Air Force Reserve (AFRES), TAC comprises over 4,000 aircraft (44 per cent of all USAF aircraft) and 188,000 personnel. It is divided into three numbered air forces and three major direct reporting units.

At a time of peaceful change in Eastern Europe, and with calls for force reductions leading to major cuts in the Air Force's units in the area, it is worth taking the time to reappraise the role that TAC has had over the last 40 years and the role it will have as we enter the 21st century.

Following the end of World War II, the Army Air Force prepared to hand over control to the new separate Air Force. On 21 March 1946 the Continental Air Forces were reorganized and redesignated by function, and so the three new Commands were created: Strategic Air Command, Tactical Air Command, and Air Defense Command. These three Commands were to provide the basic structure of the flying arm of the new Air Force which was to become operational 18 months later, on 18 September 1947.

Above: A P-47C taxies past a B-17E

Left: (From top) an F-15, A-10A and F-16C of the 57th FWW, Nellis AFB

Tactical Air Command was to be responsible for tactical operations and training, while Air Defense Command was given responsibility for the air protection of mainland America. This state of affairs carried on with minor changes until the latter, now renamed Aerospace Defense Command, was amalgamated with Tactical Air Command on 1 December 1979. TAC also gained the United States Air Force's Southern Command which had its headquarters at Albrook AFB in the Panama Canal Zone.

Although TAC itself has not been involved in a major war, it has trained and supplied many of the units that became involved in Korea and Vietnam.

Over the last 40 years TAC has been in an almost continual state of change as new aircraft have entered service and old ones have either been handed on to the ANG or AFRES or taken out of service completely. The situation has now changed in that ANG and AFRES units now receive the same aircraft that are operated by TAC and the other Commands.

The tactical aircraft that have served with the Air Force can be divided into four main groups. The first generation were the last of the prop-driven aircraft and the first jet aircraft; these served from the end of the war until the middle of the 1950's. Within this group were aircraft like the F-82 Twin Mustang and F-86 Sabre Jet. This group was followed by the Century Series fighters with aircraft like the F-100 Super Sabre and the later F-106 Delta Dart.

The F-4 heralded a new generation, out of which have grown aircraft like the McDonnell Douglas F-15 and the General Dynamics F-16. And today we are seeing the arrival of another new generation of aircraft designed to be invisible to modern radars and able to survive in a harsh electronic warfare environment, the first of which is the F-117, which took part in the invasion of Panama in late 1989. Its ability to operate unseen and to hit targets with extreme precision has heralded a revolution in aircraft design.

The F-117 will be followed into service by the winner of the Advanced Tactical Fighter (ATF) competition between the designs from the Lockheed and Northrop teams. The ATF prototypes will make their first flights in 1990 and the final ATF will enter service with approximately 750 aircraft in the middle of the decade.

Alongside the development of new aircraft has been the development of air-to-air and air-to-ground missiles. The early missiles could only be fired from directly behind an enemy aircraft while the missiles of today are capable of attack from any quarter.

Tactics have been forced to change as the aerial battlefield has grown more complex, while the number of aircraft involved has been reduced. The training needed to make use of the new aircraft, weapons and tactics has also become a much more important part of a modern pilot's life.

The system has changed but the men and women of Tactical Air Command have continued to strive for the highest levels of training and achievement, and it is those people who will carry TAC forward into the 21st century. The shape of the Command may change as forces in Europe are reduced, but TAC will always have a role in shaping the Air Force's Tactical Commands wherever they may operate in the future.

The Development of the Tactical Air Command

In 1945 the Army Air Force had a total of 2,282,259 personnel but by the following year this figure had come down to 455,515. To cope with a peacetime organization and to prepare for the eventual arrival of the new independent Air Force, the Army Air Force commanders, led by General Arnold, undertook the reorganization of the Continental Air Forces which became operational on 21 March 1946.

The Continental Air Forces were divided and redesignated by function into the Strategic, Tactical, and Air Defense Commands. Tactical Air Command was assigned the tactical Ninth Air Force as the bulk of its forces and was tasked with tactical operations and training, while the new Air Defense Command provided the air defense of mainland America. Strategic Command was responsible for all strategic bombing operations including the new weapon of mass destruction, the atomic bomb. This move was designed to provide a framework for the new Air Force which was to become operational on 18 September 1947 with General Carl Spaatz as its Chief of Staff.

The new Air Force ended 1947 with its tactical air forces equipped with a total of only 350 fighters, including 180 F-80 Shooting Stars; its strategic forces had a grand total of 319 B-29s. It was felt in Washington, DC, that as America was the only nation to possess the atomic bomb it would never have to fight another war, and for this reason Congress saw no need to waste good money on the armed forces when they would never be needed again.

Tactical Air Command's first Commander was Lt General E.R. Quesada, who commanded from 21 March 1946 until 23 November 1948. He was tasked with preparing the new Command for the arrival of the new jet fighters and ground attack aircraft which were just starting to enter service, while at the same time oversee the reduction in his Command's personnel to a peacetime level. He established his headquarters at Langley Field, Virginia (redesignated Langley AFB in 1947).

At the same time, Lt General George Stratemayer became head of the Air Defense Command. The reduction in forces was larger than originally planned, and by December 1948, both Commands had been reduced to such a level that they lost their Major Command Status. Both were integrated into a new Command, the Continental Air Command (CONAC), which was given overall command of air activities within mainland America. On 11 June 1948 a new method of designating aircraft types was introduced; the prefix P (Pursuit) was changed to F (Fighter) and the Photo Reconnaissance F became R.

Tensions in Europe saw the first real rift between the wartime Allies. In June 1947 the Soviet Army and East Germany imposed a surface blockade to the western sector of Berlin. Allied response was quick and a huge airlift was organized by the Americans, British, and French to supply the beleaguered city. This occurred at a time when the Air Force was at its lowest strength since before Pearl Harbor and the US Air Force in Europe had just lost its strategic role.

The Chief of Staff, General Hoyt Vandenberg, and Stuart Symington the Undersecretary of War for Air, lobbied Congress for more forces – both men and machines – and a slow build-up was allowed. This was to come none too soon, because as the Berlin crisis was being resolved in Europe in 1949, the Soviets detonated their first atomic bomb in the east. If that was not bad enough, in Korea trouble flared up, and on 25 June 1950 the communist North Korean forces invaded southern Korea. One of the results of the invasion was that in December CONAC was broken up and TAC and ADC were again made separate Major Commands. They would stay that way until they were again merged as a single Tactical Air Command in 1979. It was obvious that TAC would have to prepare large numbers of squadrons which could be shipped to Korea. It was also obvious that the Soviet Union was prepared to challenge America's number one position in the world, and it was imperative that America should be prepared on all fronts.

The South Korean forces were quickly pushed back and Americans were evacuated under the cover of Fifth Air Force fighters and bombers. Although in the first days the war was being won in the air, on the ground it was another matter and Seoul fell to the advancing enemy. The United Nations, meeting in emergency session on 7 July 1950, established a unified Military Command lead

Below: A foursome of Lockheed F-80Cs of the 36th FBS

Below: An 18th FBW F-86 being re-armed at Osan, Korea

by the United States which would go to South Korea's aid.

The American Air Forces in the region, operating from bases in Japan and Okinawa, attacked North Korea and quickly reduced the North's industrial power base to rubble. On 15 September General MacArthur's troops started to land at Inchon, behind the North Korean line, while General Walker's Eighth Army counterattacked from its position at Pusan. Just over a month later it looked like the war had been won; by 26 October UN forces had reached the North Korean border with China.

Everyone started to pack up ready to return home, when suddenly on 1 November Chinese MiGs were encountered by Fifth Air Force aircraft. Within weeks the Chinese had counter-attacked and by 15 December the UN forces had been pushed back over the 38th parallel. Seoul fell to the communists for the second time on 4 January 1951 and the UN forces were pushed farther south.

As many armies had discovered in the past, the Chinese found that their supply lines had been stretched too far, and were vulnerable to air attack. UN forces, led by the US Eighth Army, started to push the Chinese back to the 38th parallel where for the next two and a half years the two sides were held in a stalemate. Peace of a sort came with the signing of the ceasefire on 27 July 1953.

The main aircraft of America's tactical air forces in the region at the start of the war was the F-80. This was to prove successful against the small North Korean Air Force but was no match for the Chinese MiG-15s, and for a period control of the air was gained by the Chinese. To combat this new menace, the Air Force quickly delivered F-86s to the Fifth Air Force, the first aircraft arriving in Korea on 1 December 1950. They flew operationally for the first time on 16 December and on the 17th they claimed their first MiG. The F-86 made a major contribution to the war effort and air superiority was regained. By the time the war came to a close, pilots flying the F-86 had shot down 792 MiGs for the loss of only 78 Sabre Jets.

The period after the Korean War saw a slow but steady build-up of the Air Force's personnel. This was a period of real Cold War tension when it seemed that World War III would erupt at any moment. For

Above: F-80Cs operating over Korea toward the end of 1952

Below: F-86Fs climb away from their Osan, Korea, base

TAC and ADC, it was a period of consolidation. The Century series started to arrive at the end of the Korean conflict while the Soviets were fielding the MiG-17, armed with four AA-1 "Alkali" guided missiles, and the strategic Tupolev Tu-16, powered by the Mikulin bureau's massive AM-3 turbojets, which entered service in 1955.

At home Air Defense Command was being armed to meet the threat of long-range Soviet bombers capable of dropping a nuclear bomb on mainland America. To aid ADC in its task a chain of radars was established throughout the USA and Canada during the 1950's. The Semi-Automatic Ground Environment (SAGE) Air Defense System was designed at the Lincoln Laboratories of the Massachusetts Institute of Technology in conjunction with ADC. SAGE was more than just a radar chain, taking in information from a wide range of sensors, including ADC's EC-121 airborne early warning aircraft. Using centralized data processing, SAGE personnel were able to control interceptor aircraft to a degree that had never before been achieved.

The new generation of aircraft were attaining speeds which meant that only missiles were considered capable of destroying enemy aircraft, and the new generation of supersonic interceptors were built without guns. The two new major missile systems were the Falcon series and the Genie unguided missiles, equipped with 1.5 kT nuclear warheads. The Falcon first entered service on the F-89H in January 1956 and the Genie on the F-89J in the same year. The F-89J was equipped with two Genies and four Falcons mounted under the wings, and the F-89H was armed with 42 Mighty Mouse rockets and six Falcons mounted in its wing pods.

Air Defense Command received its first supersonic interceptor, the F-102 Delta Dagger, in 1955 and acquired a total of 875 between then and 1957. It was armed with six AIM-4 Falcon missiles. Normally it would also carry three semi-active radar-guided AIM-4As or 4Es and three infrared homing AIM-4Cs or 4Fs. By the early 1960's the F-102 was fitted with a SAGE data link which allowed ground control direct access to the aircraft's MG-3 or the later MG-10 fire control system and the aircraft's autopilot.

Above: Convair's F-102A interceptor releasing a salvo of AIM-4 Falcon missiles

Above: The very effective F-106As saw service 1959–88

Above: McDonnell's twin-engined F-101B with braking 'chute deployed

Above: An extremely rare picture of a TAC Lockheed F-104C

The F-102 was replaced in front-line service by the F-106 Delta Dart which carried six AIM-4s and also two AIR-2A Genie unguided rockets. The Delta Dagger was finally withdrawn from regular service in 1987 and from the ANG in 1988.

Operational alongside the F-106 was the F-101B Voodoo which had been planned as a Strategic Air Command long-range escort fighter. This plan was scrapped but the F-101A and the F-101C entered service with Tactical Air Command, while the interceptor F-101B went to ADC who received more than 400 of the type. The Voodoo was used in both the interceptor role by TAC and as the RF-101A and C unarmed tactical reconnaissance.

The Lockheed F-104 Starfighter served in both ADC and TAC although for only comparatively short periods. It was used by ADC during 1958–59 and again briefly in 1963, and TAC deployed one wing of F-104C fighter-bombers armed with tactical nuclear weapons between 1958 and 1965.

TAC was again called upon to supply units abroad in 1961 when the Berlin Wall was being constructed. The 479th TFW, with its three squadrons of F-104Cs, was moved to France. Ten ANG squadrons of F-84F and F-86H fighter-bombers and RF-84F photo reconnaissance fighters were also deployed. Although the ANG units were withdrawn the following year they left enough of their aircraft to be used by a newly formed TAC wing, the 366th TFW.

In October 1962 President Kennedy revealed to the world that Soviet bombers and missiles were being stationed in Cuba. All US units around the world were alerted and Tactical Air Command moved its Composite Air Strike Force to reinforce bases in Florida. The Russians were forced to back down but for six days the world hovered on the edge of nuclear war.

The armed forces were stood down but within a few years American troops were again facing communist threat. America had started to supply military advisors to South Vietnam in a bid to stem the infiltration of communist supporters over Vietnam's demilitarized zone. The first unit to arrive was the 4400th Combat Crew Training Squadron which had been formed at Eglin AFB, Florida, in April 1961. They deployed to Bien Hoa AB under the codename Farm

Above: A flight of North American F-100Ds operating over Vietnam

Gate, and operated a mix of T-28s, EC-47s and RB-26s flown in South Vietnamese Air Force marking. They were quickly followed by small Pacific Air Forces (PACAF) detachments which deployed to Tan Son Nhut AB. Although these units did get involved in the fighting they were nominally there in an advisory role. The following year the numbers of advisors grew with the replacement of the old Military Assistance Advisory Group by the Military Assistance Command.

Vietnam (MACV), and in 1963 a full squadron of F-100D Super Sabres deployed from Clark AFB to Da Nang, bringing American forces to 15,000 in total.

The politics of the region were slowly drawing America into direct support of the South. In August 1964, the North Vietnamese attacked a US destroyer in the Gulf of Tonkin. This led to President Johnson gaining Congressional approval to take any action that he deemed fit in the protection of US Forces and of any member country of the Southeast Asia Treaty Organization.

Tactical Air Command and PACAF units were deployed to Thailand to form two new Tactical Fighter Wings, the 388th TFW at Korat and the 355th TFW at Tahkli. TAC also deployed the 3rd TFW with three F-100D squadrons to Bien Hoa AB, near Saigon. These and other PACAF units were involved in Operation Rolling Thunder against selected North Vietnamese targets. The theory behind the operation was that it would encourage the North Vietnamese to stop their raids on the South. In this it was not successful.

And so the build-up continued, with TAC in 1966 supplying F-4C units to build the 366th TFW at Da Nang, and two F-100D wings – the 31st TFW at Tuy Hoa and the 35th TFW at Phan Rang. The operations over North Vietnam and Laos were taking a heavy toll on the Air Force; during 1966, PACAF lost 379 aircraft, 126 of which were F-105s.

The growth within PACAF continued and by the beginning of 1967 it was the Air Force's second largest Major Command with a total of almost 1,700 aircraft. Rolling Thunder's list of targets was widened and new targets included the North Vietnamese Air Force interceptor bases, rail links with China and the port of Haiphong, and targets much closer to Hanoi.

The bombing still had very little effect and on 31 March 1968 President Johnson suspended all bombing of North Vietnam beyond the 20th parallel. By November all action against the North came to a halt, as the attention switched to attacking the supply lines along the Ho Chi Minh Trail through Laos. By mid-1968 over half a million US personnel were stationed in Vietnam; at this point peace talks began.

Below: This F-4D releases rockets against a VietCong target from low level

By 1969 a program of "Vietnamization" was under way, with equipment being handed over from American units to their South Vietnamese counterparts, which allowed a decline in American forces. PACAF re-established many of its units in Thailand and from there they carried on missions against the communist forces.

By 1972 PACAF strength had fallen to 20,000 personnel in South Vietnam and 27,000 in Thailand. The North Vietnamese upped the stakes again in March when they opened a new offensive against the South. The USAF reacted quickly and four F-4D squadrons from the 49th TFW based at Holloman, AFB, New Mexico, deployed to Thailand. They were accompanied by four F-4E squadrons from Seymour Johnson AFB, Texas, and Holloman and Eglin AFBs in Florida. Within a week of leaving their bases in America they had entered the conflict in support of the South Vietnamese. They attacked targets both in South and North Vietnam with some success. The aircraft were now armed with laser-guided bombs and carried jammer pods to counter radar-guided missiles. They were also supported by F-105G Wild Weasels equipped with improved countermeasures equipment and radar-homing missiles.

In September 1972 two F-111A squadrons were deployed for the second time. In their first tour, in 1968, the F-111As had suffered a number of losses which led to the aircraft being grounded, the problem being later identified as a failure of the wing pivot fitting. The F-111's ability to fly at extreme low level using terrain-following radar in all weathers and at night proved a great success. On 8 November they hit targets in North Vietnam in such bad weather that no other aircraft were able to leave the ground.

Although the bombing of North Vietnam continued with Operation Linebacker II during December 1972 and January 1973, the war was lost and a peace treaty was signed in January 1973. The Air Force kept a number of units in Thailand until 1975 when the remaining units returned either to the US or to South Korea.

As the war in South East Asia was drawing to a close, changes were taking place back home. There was a plan during the mid-1970's to bring Pacific Air Forces (PACAF) under TAC control. This was due to happen by 1 July 1975, but the order was withheld and finally abandoned 11 months later. It is possible that the 1990's will see all Tactical Commands being

brought under control as the sort of Commands like US Air Forces in Europe (USAFE) are reduced in size.

Air Defense Command had shrunk from 28 squadrons on 1 January 1968, when it was renamed Aerospace Defense Command, to only seven squadrons in 1974. Aerospace Defense Command had continued to be responsible for the nation's air defense and was a major component in joint US-Canadian North American Air

Defense Command (NORAD). It finally ceased as a separate Command on 1 December 1979, when it was split into two distinct areas. The flying squadrons became Air Defense, Tactical Air Command (ADTAC). Within this, four Divisions controlled the air defense radars, including the Distant Early Warning (DEW) line from Alaska to Greenland, and each was responsible for one of the four NORAD districts within mainland America. The other component, consisting of

Above: A Distant Early Warning System radar station in inhospitable Alaska
Below: A fine in-flight study of a Nellis-based F-111A

ADC's worldwide communications, early warning and Spacetrack, was established as the Aerospace Defense Center based at Peterson AFB, Colorado. It lasted for only three years as a separate entity before it became part of the new Space Command on 1 September 1982.

The final growth within TAC came when USAF Southern Command was merged with TAC in June 1979. It had been raised as the Caribbean Air Command in November 1947 and was the successor to the World War II Sixth Air Force. It was responsible for the South Atlantic approaches and was redesignated USAFSO in July 1963. With the arrival of Southern Command, TAC had gained control of all tactical air assets in continental USA, as far south as Panama and east to Iceland.

TAC today provides the air component of the United States Readiness Command (USREDCOM), US Central Command (USCENTCOM), US Atlantic Command (LANTCOM), and the US Southern Command (SOUTHCOM). It also supports the US European Command (USEUCOM) and the US Pacific Command (USPACOM).

The Commander of the Tactical Air Command also wears two other hats: Commander-in-Chief, Air Force Readiness Command (CINCAFRED) and Commander-in-Chief, Air Forces Atlantic (CINCAFLANT).

To fulfill these tasks TAC is divided into three numbered air forces: the First Air Force with its headquarters at Langley AFB; the Ninth whose headquarters are at Shaw AFB; and the 12th controlled from Bergstrom AFB. It also has the 28th Air Division, responsible for airborne warning and control, and the Tactical Fighter Weapons and Tactical Air Warfare Centers.

Langley AFB became TAC's headquarters in May 1946 and is also home to TAC's First Air Force, whose Commander is also head of the Continental United States (CONUS) North American Aerospace Defense Region of NORAD. The First Air Force underwent a major command reshuffle in 1987, when its four air divisions were rearranged. It is now made up of two air divisions each of which is divided into two air defense sectors. The 24th Air Division, with its headquarters at Griffiss AFB, NY, has control of the Northeast Air Defense Sector based at Griffiss, and the Southeast Air Defense Sector based at Tyndall AFB, Florida. The 25th Air Division has its headquarters at McChord AFB, Washington, and covers the west coast. The Northwest Air Defense Sector is located at McChord and the Southwest Air Defense sector is at March AFB, California. The 24th Air Division also has the Air Forces Iceland which operate F-15s from Keflavik NS, and the USAF Air Defense Weapons Center at Tyndall AFB.

The 24th Air Division was the last regular unit to fly the F-106 and these were retired during 1987. Other aircraft in the First include

Below: A Tupolev "Bear" receiving attention from two Keflavik-based F-15Cs of the 57th FIS

F-4C/Ds, F-15s and F-16s. The First Air Force maintains the Air Forces Iceland at Keflavik Naval Station. Its F-15s fly valuable interceptor missions along the arctic circle. As one of its contributions to NORAD the 4700th Air Defense Squadron operates the DEW Line radar sites. Also contained in the First AF is the USAF Air Defense Weapons Center (USAFADWC) located at Tyndall AFB, Florida. Its role is to train aircrews and weapons controllers, develop air defense tactics, and manage all CONUS USAF drone aerial target operations. It is made up of the 325th Tactical Training Wing and the 475th Weapons Evaluation Group.

The Ninth Air Force, with its headquarters at Shaw AFB, operates a variety of fighter and attack aircraft. These include A-10s flown by the 23rd and 354th Tactical Fighter Wings. F-4s are flown by the 4th, 31st and 347th TFWs. The F-15s are flown by the 1st and 33rd TFWs, and F-16s are operated by the 31st, 347th and 363rd TFWs and the 56th Tactical Training Wing. The 363rd also operates the RF-4C reconnaissance aircraft.

The largest of TAC's Air Forces is the Twelfth which has its headquarters at Bergstrom AFB. The Twelfth is made up of five air divisions, of which four are training wings dedicated to each of USAF's front-line fighters and attack aircraft, plus the 868th Tactical Missile Training Group at Davis-Monthan which trains GLCM crews. The USAF Southern Air Division (USAFSO), based at Howard AFB in Panama, provides air defense for the Panama Canal. The Division also provides training facilities for South American air forces.

The 28th Air Division, based at Tinker AFB, Oklahoma, operates TAC's fleet of E-3 AWACS which operate over mainland America, Alaska, Iceland and Japan. It also

Left: A-10As of the 345th TFW, Myrtle Beach AFB
Above: The Boeing E-3A Sentry, highlighted by a low, northern sun

has a detachment in Saudi Arabia in support of Saudi E-3s. The 552nd AWCW has now logged more than 5,000 missions, clocking up more than 67,000 hours, while operational in the Persian Gulf. It also operates EC-130s for airborne battlefield command and control and as a jamming platform against enemy C³ networks. EC-135s are operated by the 8th Tactical Deployment Squadron, and are used as flying command posts and to provide assistance for overseas deployments of tactical fighters.

Tactical Air Command also has two Weapons Centers. The USAF Tactical Fighter Weapons Center (USAFTFWC) at Nellis AFB is concerned with advanced training and developing new tactical air combat concepts, the doctrine of air warfare and the testing of new weapons systems. It is host unit for Red Flag exercises and is also home

Below: General Dynamics F-16Cs of the Nellis-based USAF Thunderbirds team

of the USAF Air Demonstration Squadron (The Thunderbirds). The other Weapons Center is the USAF Tactical Air Warfare Center (USAFTAWC) at Eglin AFB which works on similar lines to the USAFTFWC but is concerned with the electronic battlefield. It also organizes the Green Flag program of exercises.

To provide realistic training TAC operates a number of specialist exercises. These "Flag" exercises include the following:
Black Flag is designed to train aircraft maintenance crews to operate under wartime conditions and still keep their aircraft flying.
Blue Flag exercises are dedicated to real-time Command, Control and Communications training. They are designed to cover all areas of the world where USAF operates and are used not only by TAC personnel but by other branches of USAF, US Army and Navy personnel, and other Allied air forces.
Checkered Flag is designed to

enable TAC fighter squadrons and tactical air control units to prepare for operations from their assigned overseas bases. Units and personnel are regularly deployed to these bases so that they can operate efficiently in times of crisis.
Copper Flag exercises, based at Tyndall AFB, are used to increase the readiness of air defense forces using simulated enemy attacks.
Green Flag is operated by USAFTAWC (USAF Tactical Air Warfare Center) and USAFTFWC (USAF Tactical Fighter Weapons Center). These exercises are designed to test and train aircrew to operate and survive in a hostile electronic warfare environment.
Red Flag is the most famous of the Flag programs. Its exercises are a regular part of life at Nellis AFB, providing tactical fighter training against simulated enemy air and ground forces. Up to 300 aircraft can be involved in a Red Flag exercise, the pilots and aircraft coming from all Commands of the

Air Force, US Navy and Marine Corps, NATO and other Allied air forces. In overall charge of the exercise is the 4440th Tactical Fighter Training Group which organizes each exercise from Building 201 at Nellis AFB. The tactics used are determined by the Adversary Tactics Directorate, the parent unit of the two former Aggressor squadrons based at Nellis, the 64th and 65th AS who flew their Soviet colored F-16s. (The F-16s are now being returned to normal duty.) Once a year a Green Flag exercise is held in conjunction with Red Flag.
Silver Flag is designed for combat support units to operate in a hostile environment. They are set a variety of combat problems that they might be tasked with in a combat or emergency situation.

Right: Camera gun playback, and 3-dimensional computer-generated graphics help train advanced fighter pilots at Nellis AFB

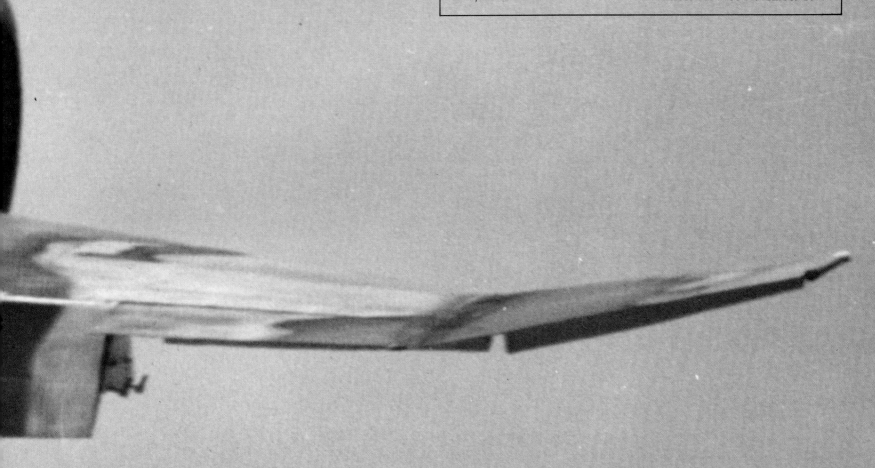

Commanders of the Tactical Air Command

Lt Gen E.R. Quesada	21 March 1946–23 November 1948
Maj Gen Robert Lee	24 December 1948–20 June 1950
Maj Gen Glenn Barcus	17 July 1950–25 January 1951
Gen John Cannon	25 January 1951–31 March 1954
Gen O.P. Wayland	1 April 1954–31 July 1959
Gen Frank Everest	1 August 1959–30 September 1961
Gen Walter Sweeney, Jr	1 October 1961–31 July 1965
Gen Gabriel Disosway	1 August 1965–31 July 1968
Gen William Momyer	1 August 1968–30 September 1973
Gen Robert Dixon	1 October 1973–30 April 1978
Gen W.L. Creech	1 May 1978–1 November 1984
Gen Jerome F. O'Malley	1 November 1984–20 April 1985
Gen Robert D. Ross	22 May 1985–

Commanders of the Air Defense Command

Lt Gen George Stratemayer	21 March 1946–30 November 1948
Maj Gen Gordon Saville	1 December 1948–31 December 1950
Lt Gen Ennis Whitehead	1 January 1951–25 August 1951
Gen Benjamin Chidlaw	25 August 1951–31 May 1955
Maj Gen Frederick Smith, Jr	31 May 1955–19 July 1955 (acting)
Gen Earle Partridge	20 July 1955–17 September 1956
Lt Gen Joseph Atkinson	17 September 1956–15 August 1961
Lt Gen Robert Lee	15 August 1961–31 July 1963
Lt Gen Herbert Thatcher	1 August 1963–31 July 1967
Lt Gen Arthur Agan	1 August 1967–31 December 1967

Commanders of the Aerospace Command

Lt Gen Arthur Agan	1 January 1968–28 February 1970
Lt Gen Thomas McGehee	1 March 1970–1 July 1973
Gen Seth McKee	1 July 1973–1 October 1973
Gen Lucius Clay, Jr	1 October 1973–31 August 1975
Gen Daniel James, Jr	1 September 1975–5 December 1977
Gen James Hill	6 December 1977–30 November 1979

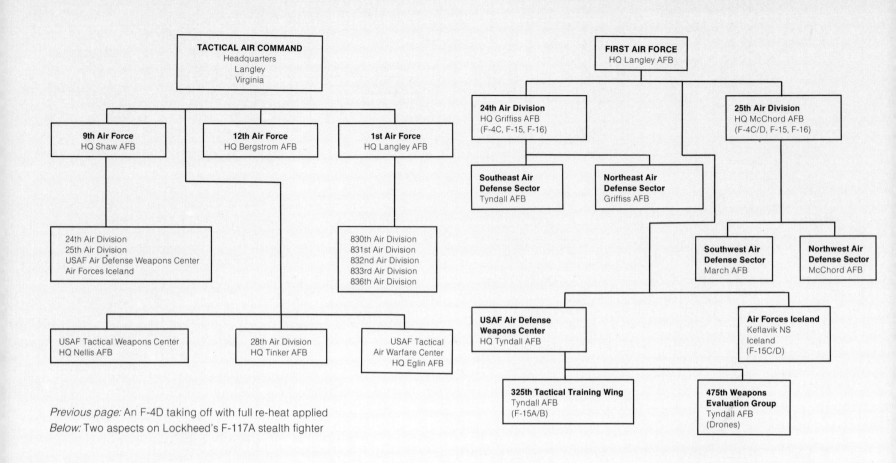

TACTICAL AIR COMMAND
Headquarters
Langley
Virginia

9th Air Force
HQ Shaw AFB

12th Air Force
HQ Bergstrom AFB

1st Air Force
HQ Langley AFB

24th Air Division
25th Air Division
USAF Air Defense Weapons Center
Air Forces Iceland

830th Air Division
831st Air Division
832nd Air Division
833rd Air Division
836th Air Division

USAF Tactical Weapons Center
HQ Nellis AFB

28th Air Division
HQ Tinker AFB

USAF Tactical
Air Warfare Center
HQ Eglin AFB

FIRST AIR FORCE
HQ Langley AFB

24th Air Division
HQ Griffiss AFB
(F-4C, F-15, F-16)

25th Air Division
HQ McChord AFB
(F-4C/D, F-15, F-16)

**Southeast Air
Defense Sector**
Tyndall AFB

**Northeast Air
Defense Sector**
Griffiss AFB

**Southwest Air
Defense Sector**
March AFB

**Northwest Air
Defense Sector**
McChord AFB

**USAF Air Defense
Weapons Center**
HQ Tyndall AFB

Air Forces Iceland
Keflavik NS
Iceland
(F-15C/D)

325th Tactical Training Wing
Tyndall AFB
(F-15A/B)

**475th Weapons
Evaluation Group**
Tyndall AFB
(Drones)

Previous page: An F-4D taking off with full re-heat applied
Below: Two aspects on Lockheed's F-117A stealth fighter

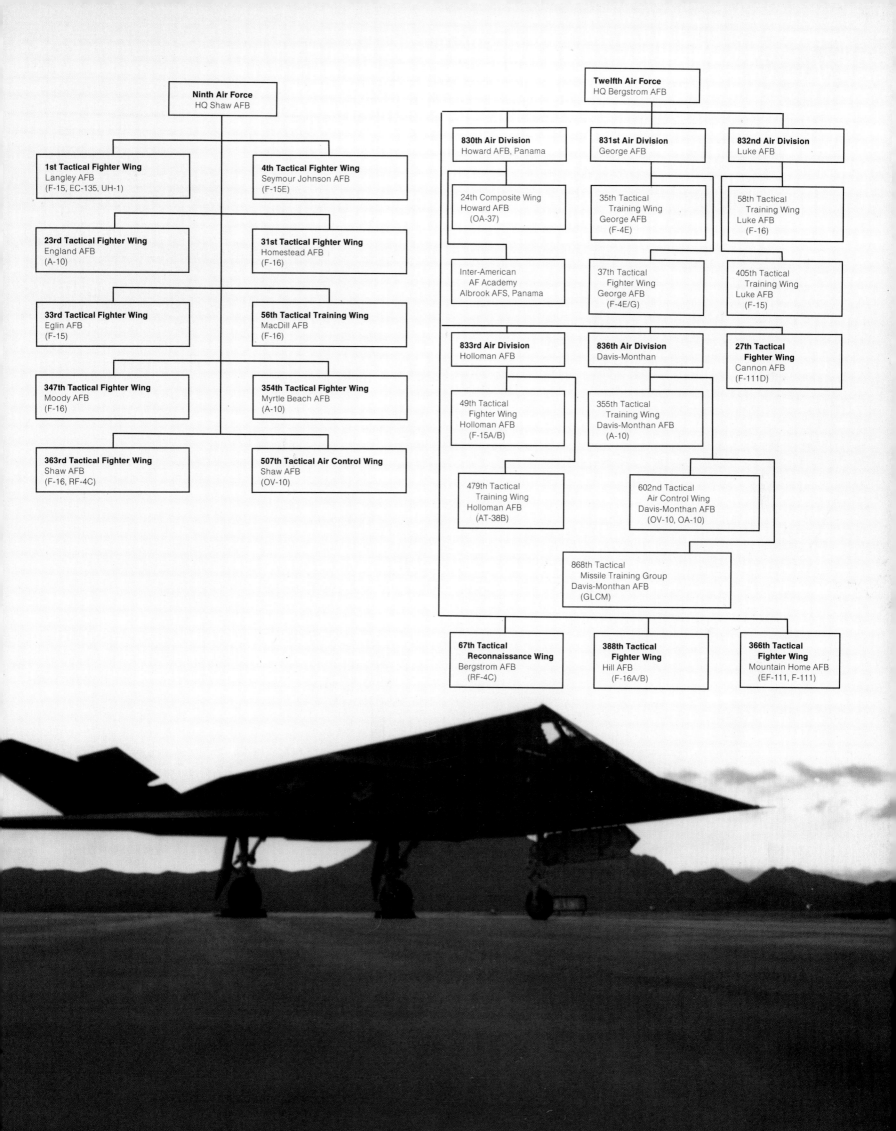

Ninth Air Force
HQ Shaw AFB

1st Tactical Fighter Wing
Langley AFB
(F-15, EC-135, UH-1)

4th Tactical Fighter Wing
Seymour Johnson AFB
(F-15E)

23rd Tactical Fighter Wing
England AFB
(A-10)

31st Tactical Fighter Wing
Homestead AFB
(F-16)

33rd Tactical Fighter Wing
Eglin AFB
(F-15)

56th Tactical Training Wing
MacDill AFB
(F-16)

347th Tactical Fighter Wing
Moody AFB
(F-16)

354th Tactical Fighter Wing
Myrtle Beach AFB
(A-10)

363rd Tactical Fighter Wing
Shaw AFB
(F-16, RF-4C)

507th Tactical Air Control Wing
Shaw AFB
(OV-10)

Twelfth Air Force
HQ Bergstrom AFB

830th Air Division
Howard AFB, Panama

831st Air Division
George AFB

832nd Air Division
Luke AFB

24th Composite Wing
Howard AFB
(OA-37)

35th Tactical
Training Wing
George AFB
(F-4E)

58th Tactical
Training Wing
Luke AFB
(F-16)

Inter-American
AF Academy
Albrook AFS, Panama

37th Tactical
Fighter Wing
George AFB
(F-4E/G)

405th Tactical
Training Wing
Luke AFB
(F-15)

833rd Air Division
Holloman AFB

836th Air Division
Davis-Monthan

**27th Tactical
Fighter Wing**
Cannon AFB
(F-111D)

49th Tactical
Fighter Wing
Holloman AFB
(F-15A/B)

355th Tactical
Training Wing
Davis-Monthan AFB
(A-10)

479th Tactical
Training Wing
Holloman AFB
(AT-38B)

602nd Tactical
Air Control Wing
Davis-Monthan AFB
(OV-10, OA-10)

868th Tactical
Missile Training Group
Davis-Monthan AFB
(GLCM)

**67th Tactical
Reconnaissance Wing**
Bergstrom AFB
(RF-4C)

**388th Tactical
Fighter Wing**
Hill AFB
(F-16A/B)

**366th Tactical
Fighter Wing**
Mountain Home AFB
(EF-111, F-111)

Bases

Bergstrom

Bergstrom AFB
Texas 78743–5000
USA

Phone:
(512) 479–4100

Autovon:
685–1100

Area located:
11 km (7 miles) east of central Austin, situated on State Highway 71

Command:
Tactical Air Command

Date est:
September 1942

Named after:
Capt John A.E. Bergstrom who was killed at Clark Field, Philippines, on 8 December 1941

Acreage:
3,998

Personnel:
4,951 military personnel, 1,054 civilians

Units:
HQ 12th Air Force; 67th Tactical Reconnaissance Wing, 12th Tactical Reconnaissance Squadron, 45th Tactical Reconnaissance Training Squadron, 62nd Tactical Reconnaissance Training Squadron, 91st Tactical Reconnaissance Squadron; HQ 10th Air Force (AFRES); 924th Tactical Fighter Group (AFRES), 704th Tactical Fighter Squadron; TAC NCO Academy West; Det 8, 602nd Tactical Air Control Wing; Det 1, 4400th Management Engineering Squadron; Det 12, Tactical Communications Division

Operational aircraft:
67th Tactical Reconnaissance Wing (TAC)
RF-4C   12th TRS   (BA)
      45th TRTS
      62nd TRTS
      91st TRS
704th Tactical Fighter Squadron (AFRES)
F-4D   (TX)

Below: An RF-4C of the type operated by the 67th TRW, Bergstrom AFB

Cannon

Cannon AFB
New Mexico 88103–5000
USA

Phone:
(505) 784–3311

Autovon:
681–1110

Area located:
11 km (7 miles) west of Clovis, situated on US 60/84

Command:
Tactical Air Command

Date est:
August 1942

Named after:
General John K. Cannon, one of America's leaders in the development of air power. He served as commander of Allied air forces in the Mediterranean during the later stages of World War II

Acreage:
25,663

Personnel:
3,650 military personnel, 782 civilians

Units:
27th Tactical Fighter Wing, 522nd Tactical Fighter Squadron, 523rd Tactical Fighter Squadron, 524th Tactical Fighter Squadron; 2040th Communications Squadron

Operational aircraft:
27th Tactical Fighter Wing (TAC)
F–111D   522nd TFS   (CC)
        523rd TFS
        524th TFS

Above right: An F-111D on delivery to Cannon AFB's 27th TFW

Davis-Monthan

Davis-Monthan AFB
Arizona 85707–5000
USA

Phone:
(602) 750–3900

Autovon:
361–1110

Area located:
Within the southeast area of the city of Tucson, located off 1–10

Command:
Tactical Air Command

Date est:
1927

Named after:
1st Lt Samuel H. Davis and 2nd Lt Oscar Monthan, both killed in flying accidents during the early 1920's

Acreage:
11,000

Personnel:
5,725 military personnel, 1,499 civilians

Units:
836th Air Division; 355th Tactical Training Wing, 333rd Tactical Fighter Training Squadron, 357th Tactical Fighter Training Squadron, 358th Tactical Fighter Training Squadron; 602nd Tactical Air Control Wing, 23rd Tactical Air Support Squadron; 868th TAC Missile Training Group; 71st SOS; 836th Combat Support Group; 41st Electronic Combat Squadron; Det 1, 120th Fighter Interceptor Group (ANG); 71st Special Operations Squadron (AFRES); Military Aerospace Maintenance and Regeneration Center (AFLC)

Operational aircraft:
602nd Tactical Air Control Wing
OA-37B   23rd TASS (TAC)
OA-10A   (NF)
EC-130H 41st ECS (TAC)   (DM)
355th Tactical Training Wing (TAC)
A-10A   333rd TFTS
        357th TFTS
        358th TFTS   (DM)
71st Special Operations Squadron
CH/HH-3E

Notes:
The 868th TAC Missile Training Group trains for Ground Launched Cruise Missiles. The 23rd TASS is currently converting to the OA-10A

Left: The end of a GLCM. All US missile demolition takes place at Davis-Monthan AFB

Eglin

Eglin AFB
Florida 32542–5000
USA

Phone:
(904) 881–6668

Autovon:
872–1110

Command:
Air Force Systems Command

Date Est:
1935

Named after:
Lt Col Frederick I. Eglin, a World War I flyer killed in an air crash in 1937

Acreage:
464,980

Personnel:
9,916 military personnel, 4,791 civilians, plus 950 contractor staff

Units:
Air Force Armament Division; Air Force Armament Test Lab; Tactical Air Warfare Center; 33rd Tactical Fighter Wing (TAC), 58th Tactical Fighter Squadron, 59th Tactical Fighter Squadron, 60th Tactical Fighter Squadron; 39th Aerospace Rescue & Recovery Wing; 55th Aerospace Rescue & Recovery Squadron; Det 4, 1402nd Military Airlift Squadron; Det 10, 2nd Weather Squadron; 1972nd Communications Squadron; 919th Special Operations Group (AFRES); 711th Special Operations Squadron (AFRES); 20th Missile Warning Squadron; 728th Tactical Control Squadron; plus a US Navy Explosive Ordnance Disposal School and the US Army Florida Ranger School

Operational aircraft:
3246th Test Wing/Armament
Division (AFSC)
Various
39th Aerospace Rescue & Recovery
Wing (MAC)
CH-3E det 5 Tyndall AFB Fla
HH-3E det 11 Myrtle AFB SC
CH-3E det 12 Patrick AFB Fla
55th Aerospace Rescue & Recovery
Squadron (MAC)
HC-130   N/P
UH-60A
33rd Tactical Fighter Wing (TAC)
F-15C/D   58th TFS   (EG)
             59th TFS
             60th TFS

Above: An F-16's APG-66 radar being checked out at Eglin AFB
Left: A 33rd TFW F-15 departs Eglin

4485th Test Squadron (TAC)
Various   (OT)
AC-130A   711th SOS

Notes:
Eglin AB is the largest air force base in the western world

England

England AFB
Louisiana 71311–5004
USA

Phone:
(318) 448–2100

Autovon:
683–1110

Area located:
8 km (5 miles) west of Alexandria, off State Highway 1 or State Highway 28

Command:
Tactical Air Command

Date est:
October 1942

Named after:
Lt Col John B. England, a World War II P-51 ace who was killed in an F-86 crash while serving in France in 1954

Acreage:
2,282

Personnel:
3,057 military personnel, 667 civilians

Units:
23rd Tactical Fighter Wing, 74th Tactical Fighter Squadron, 75th Tactical Fighter Squadron, 76th Tactical Fighter Squadron

Operational aircraft:
23rd Tactical Fighter Wing (TAC)
A-10A 74th TFS (EL)
   75th TFS
   76th TFS

George

George AFB
California 92394–5000
USA

Phone:
(619) 269–1110

Autovon:
353–1110

Area located:
Within the Mojave Desert, 9.6 km (6 miles) northwest of Victorville and 72.4 km (45 miles) north of San Bernardino

Command:
Tactical Air Command

Date est:
1941

Below: An F-4G of the 37th TFW, recently moved from George to Nellis

Named after:
Brig Gen Harold H. George, a World War I fighter ace, who died in a flying accident over Australia in 1942

Acreage:
5,347

Personnel:
5,246 military personnel, 548 civilians

Units:
831st Air Division; 561st Tactical Fighter Squadron, 562nd Tactical Fighter Squadron, 563rd Tactical Fighter Squadron; 35th Tactical Fighter Wing, 20th Tactical Fighter Training Squadron, 21st Tactical Fighter Training Squadron; OLAD, 144th FIW (TAC); 267th Communications Squadron (AFCC)

Operational aircraft:
F-4E&G 561st TFS (WW)
   562nd TFS

   563rd TFS
35th Tactical Fighter Wing (TAC)
F-4E 20th TFTS (GA)
  21st TFTS
  561st TFS
  562nd TFTS

Notes:
The 35th TFW will continue to provide training on the F-4 for German Air Force and F-4 transitional and upgrade training for the USAF. Since publication of the Report of the Defense Secretary's Commission on Base Realignments and Closures, December 1988, the Air Force has authorized the following: The base will close at the end December 1992; the 37th Tactical Fighter Wing has moved to Nellis AFB; the 35th Tactical Training Wing has been redesignated the 35th Tactical Fighter Wing and will move to Mountain Home, Idaho; the 27th Tactical Air Support Squadron was deactivated in June 1990

Gila Bend

Barry M. Goldwater AF Range
Gila Bend Air Force Auxiliary Field
Arizona 85337–5000
USA

Phone:
See Luke AFB

Autovon:
853–5520

Area located:
80 km (50 miles) southwest of
Phoenix

Command:
Tactical Air Command

Date est:
1941

Acreage:
2,700,000

Personnel:
177 military personnel, 80 civilians

Units:
832nd Combat Support Squadron

Notes:
The Field is used by Luke AFB as a
bombing and gunnery range. The
832nd are responsible for construction and maintenance of the various
target complexes

Hill

Hill AFB
Utah 84056–5990
USA

Command:
Air Force Logistics Command

Date est:
November 1940

Named after:
Major Ployer P. Hill who was killed
test flying the first B-17 in 1935

Acreage:
6,666 acres plus 961,102 acres it
manages

Personnel:
5,100 military personnel, 15,300
civilians

Units:
HQ Ogden Air Logistics Center;
388th Tactical Fighter Wing, 4th
Tactical Fighter Squadron, 34th Tactical Fighter Squadron, 421st Tacti-

cal Fighter Squadron; 419th Tactical
Fighter Wing (AFRES); 40th Aero-
space Rescue & Recovery Squadron;
729th Tactical Control Squadron;
6545th Test Group, 6514th Test
Squadron; Det 6, 17th Weather
Squadron; 1881st Communications
Squadron; 84th Radar Evaluation
Squadron

Operational aircraft:

388th Tactical Fighter Wing (TAC)		
F16A/B	4th TFS	(HL)
	34th TFS	
	421st TFS	

466th Tactical Fighter Squadron
(AFRES)

F16A/B	(HI)

6514th Test Squadron (AESC)
Various
40th Aerospace Rescue & Recovery
UH-1N   Squadron (MAC)
det 4, Hill AFB
det 6 Holloman AFB, NM
det 18 Plattsburgh AFB, NY, det 22
Mountain Home AFB Id
det 24 Fairchild AFB, Wa

Notes:
The logistics center provides sup-

Above: A mix of single-seat F-16As and
two-seat F-16Bs can be seen in this
flight line view of Hill AFB

port for Peacekeeper, Minuteman
and Titan II strategic missiles,
Maverick air-to-ground missiles,
laser and electro-optical bombs. The
unit is systems manager for the F-4
and F-16. It also handles air
munitions, aircraft landing gears,
wheels, brakes and struts, tires and
tubes, photographic and aerospace
training equipment

Holloman

Holloman AFB
New Mexico 88330–5000
USA

Phone:
(505) 479–6511

Autovon:
867–1110

Area located:
12.8 km (8 miles) southwest of
Alamogordo on Route 70/82

Command:
Tactical Air Command

Date est:
1942

Above: Mechanics work on the
hydraulics system of a 49th TFW F-15A
at Holloman AFB
Right: F-15As of the 49th TFW,
Holloman AFB, caught mirrored by
rainwater

Named after:
Col George Holloman, a guided missile pioneer who was killed in a B-17 on Formosa (now Taiwan) in 1946

Acreage:
50,697

Personnel:
5,447 military personnel, 1,756 civilians

Units:
833rd Air Division, 49th Tactical Fighter Wing; 7th Tactical Fighter Squadron, 8th Tactical Fighter Squadron, 9th Tactical Fighter Squadron; 479th Tactical Training Wing, 433rd Tactical Fighter Training Squadron, 434th Tactical Fighter Training Squadron, 435th Tactical Fighter Training Squadron, 436th Tactical Fighter Training Squadron; 4449th Mobility Support Squadron; 82nd and 83rd Tactical Control Flights; 6585th Test Group (AFSC)

conducts test and evaluation of aircraft and missile systems. There are 21 other tenant units on base including 1877th Information Systems Squadron; 4th Satellite Communications Squadron (AFSPACECOM); 1984th Communications Squadron; 40th ARRS and an Air Force Geophysical Laboratory detachment

Operational aircraft:
49th Tactical Fighter Wing (TAC)
F-15A/B   7th TFS   (HO)
             8th TFS
             9th TFS
475th Tactical Training Wing (TAC)
T-38A/AT-38B   (HM)
             433rd TFTS
             434th TFTS
             435th TFTS
             436th TFTS
93rd Tactical Fighter Squadron
             (AFRES)
HC-130H/N

Below: A General Dynamics F-16A of the type flown by Homestead's 307th TFS

Homestead

Homestead AFB
Florida 33039–5000
USA

Phone:
(305) 257–8011

Autovon:
791–8011

Command:
Tactical Air Command

Date est:
April 1955

Acreage:
3,345

Personnel:
5,139 military personnel, 1,035 civilians

Units:
31st Tactical Fighter Wing, 307th Tactical Fighter Squadron, 308th Tactical Fighter Squadron, 309th Tactical Fighter Squadron; 31st Combat Support Group; 726th Tactical Control Squadron (TAC); 482nd Tactical Fighter Wing (AFRES), 93rd Tactical Fighter Squadron (AFRES); 125th Fighter Interceptor Group (TAC); 301st Aerospace Rescue & Recovery Squadron (AFRES); ATC Sea-Survival School; Naval Security Group

Operational aircraft:
27th Tactical Fighter Wing
F-16A/B   307th TFS   (HS)
             308th TFS
             309th TFS
93rd Tactical Fighter Squadron
             (FM)
F-4D
301st Aerospace Rescue & Recovery
             Squadron (AFRES)
HC-130H/N

Right: All of TAC's E-3s operate out of Keflavik, Iceland

Howard

Howard AFB
Panama
APO Miami 34001–5000

Command:
Tactical Air Command

Date est:
1948

Units:
HQ USAF Southern Air Division;
24th Composite Squadron; 310th
Military Airlift Squadron

Operational aircraft:
24th Composite Squadron
OA-37   (HW)
310th Military Airlift Squadron
C-22A
C-130E

Indian Springs

Indian Springs Air Force Auxiliary
Field
Nevada 89018–5000
USA

Command:
Tactical Air Command

Date est:
1942

Acreage:
1,652

Personnel:
289 military personnel, 19 civilians

Units:
554th Combat Support Squadron;
4460th Helicopter Squadron

Notes:
The field supplies bombing and gunnery range support for units operating out of Nellis AFB. The 554th
are responsible for construction of
realistic targets, both vehicles and
defense works

Keesler

Keesler AFB
Mississippi 39534–5000
USA

Command:
Air Training Command

Date est:
June 1941

Named after:
2nd Lt Samuel R. Keesler, a World

War I aerial observer killed in
action near Verdun on 9 October
1918

Acreage:
3,600

Personnel:
8,933 military personnel, 2,109
civilians

Units:
Keesler Technical Training Center;
Keesler Medical Center; AFCC
Engineering Installation Group;
AFCC NCO Academy/Leadership
School; USAF First Sergeant's
Academy; 815th Weather Recon-
naissance Squadron (AFRES); 7th
Airborne Command & Control
Squadron (TAC)

Operational aircraft:
815th Weather Reconnaissance
Squadron (AFRES)
WC-130H
7th Airborne Command & Control
Squadron (TAC)
EC-130E   (KS)
(not all aircraft carry a tailcode)

Notes:
The Training Center handles communications, electronics, avionics,
radar systems, computer and
command and control systems, personnel and administration courses

Keflavik

Naval Air Station
Keflavik
Iceland
Mailing address:
US Air Forces Iceland
FPO New York 09571

Phone:
24324

Autovon:
(314) 228–0127

Command:
Tactical Air Command

Units:
US Air Forces Iceland; 57th Fighter
Interceptor Squadron (TAC); 552nd
Airborne Warning and Control
Wing detachment

Operational aircraft:
57th Fighter Interceptor Squadron
(TAC)
F-15C/D   (IS)
552nd Airborne Warning and
Control Wing (AW&CW)
E-3

Notes:
The Base is operated by the US
Navy. The E-3s are supplied on a
rotational basis from the 552nd
AW&CW at Tinker AFB, Oklahoma

Langley

Langley AFB
Virginia 23665–5000
USA

Phone:
(804) 764–9990

Autovon:
574–1110

Area located:
4.8 km (3 miles) north of Hampton
on the Virginia Peninsular situated
off 1–64

Command:
Tactical Air Command

Date est:
30 December 1916

Right: Squadron badges of Langley's
1st TFW
Below: An F-15A of the 1st TFW

Named after:
Samuel Pierpont Langley, an early air pioneer and scientist who died in 1906

Acreage:
3,439

Personnel:
9,581 military personnel, 3,000 civilians

Units:
HQ Tactical Air Command; HQ 1st Air Force (TAC); 1st Tactical Fighter Wing, 27th Tactical Fighter Squadron, 71st Tactical Fighter Squadron, 94th Tactical Fighter Squadron, 6th Airborne Command & Control Squadron; HQ CONUS NORAD; 5th Weather Wing; 2nd Aircraft Delivery Group (TAC); 1913th Communications Group (AFCC); 1912th Computer Systems Group (AFCC); 564th Air Force Band (TAC); Det 7, 3rd Weather Squadron (MAC); 48th Fighter Interceptor Squadron; 6th Airborne Command and Control Squadron (TAC); Low Intensity Conflict Center; NASA Langley Research Center; plus 20 other units

Operational aircraft:
1st Tactical Fighter Wing (TAC)
F-15C/D   27th TFS   (FF)
             71st TFS
             94th TFS
EC-135H 6th ACCS (TAC)
EC-135P
48th Fighter Interceptor Squadron (TAC)
F-15A/B

Luke

Luke AFB
Arizona 85309
USA

Phone:
(602) 856–7411

Autovon:
853–1110

Area located:
32 km (20 miles) northwest of Phoenix, and 14.5 km (9 miles) west of Glendale

Command:
Tactical Air Command

Date est:
1941

Named after:
2nd Lt Frank Luke, Jn, a World War I observation balloon-bursting ace, killed in action near Murvaux, France, in 1918. He was the first aviator to be awarded the Medal of Honor

Acreage:
4,197, plus a 2,700,000 acres range at Gila Bend

Personnel:
5,543 military personnel, 1,450 civilians

Below: F-16Cs of the 58th TTW. Luke AFB, fly in "finger-five" formation

Units:
832nd Air Division; 58th Tactical Training Wing, 310th Tactical Fighter Training Squadron, 311th Tactical Fighter Training Squadron, 312th Tactical Fighter Training Squadron, 314th Tactical Fighter Training Squadron; 405th Tactical Training Wing, 426th Tactical Fighter Training Squadron; 461st Tactical Fighter Training Squadron, 550th Tactical Fighter Training Squadron, 555th Tactical Fighter Training Squadron; 944th Tactical Fighter Group (AFRES), 302nd Tactical Fighter Squadron (AFRES); 2037th Communications Squadron

Operational aircraft:
58th Tactical Training Wing (TAC)
F-16A/B   310th TFTS
             311th TFTS
F-16C/D   312th TFTS
             314th TFTS
405th Tactical Training Wing (TAC)
F-5B/E/F 425th TFS Williams AFB
F-15/A/B 426th TFTS   (LA)
          461st TFTS
          550th TFTS
          555th TFTS

Notes:
The largest fighter training base in the western world. It trains both USAF and foreign pilots on the F-5, F-15 and F-16

MacDill

MacDill AFB
Florida 33608–5000
USA

Phone:
(813) 830–1110

Autovon:
968–1110

Area located:
South edge of the city of Tampa

Command:
Tactical Air Command

Date est:
April 1941

Named after:
Col Leslie MacDill, killed in an aircraft accident near Washington, DC, in 1938

Acreage:
5,631

Personnel:
6,849 military personnel, 1,894 civilians

Units:
56th Tactical Training Wing, 61st Tactical Fighter Training Squadron, 62nd Tactical Fighter Training Squadron, 63rd Tactical Fighter Training Squadron; HQ US Special Operations Command; HQ US Central Command; Joint Communications Support Element

Operational aircraft:
56th Tactical Training Wing (TAC)
F-16A/B   61st TFTS
           62nd TFTS
           63rd TFTS
UH-1P

Notes:
The 56th TTW is responsible for replacement training on the F-16

Left: McDill AFB serves as the home of these 56th TTW F-16As

Moody

Moody AFB
Georgia 31699–5000
USA

Phone:
(912) 333–4211

Autovon:
460–1110

Area located:
16 km (10 miles) northeast of Valdosta situated on State Highway 125

Command:
Tactical Air Command

Date est:
June 1941

Named after:
Major George P. Moody who was killed in 1941 while test-flying a Beech AT-10

Acreage:
6,050

Personnel:
3,493 Military personnel, 664 civilians

Units:
347th Tactical Fighter Wing, 68th Tactical Fighter Squadron, 69th Tactical Fighter Squadron, 70th Tactical Fighter Squadron; Det 23, 3rd Weather Squadron; 1878th Communications Squadron

Operational aircraft:
347th Tactical Fighter Wing (TAC)
F-16A/B   68th TFS   (MY)
           69th TFS
           70th TFS

Mountain Home

Mountain Home AFB
Idaho 83648–5000
USA

Phone:
(208) 828–1110

Autovon:
857/1110

Area located:
80 km (50 miles) southeast of Boise, 16 km (10 miles) southwest of Mountain Home near I-84

Command:
Tactical Air Command

Date est:
April 1942

Named after:
The town of Mountain Home

Acreage:
9,112

Personnel:
3,802 military personnel, 548 civilians

Units:
366th Tactical Fighter Wing, 389th Tactical Fighter Training Squadron, 391st Tactical Fighter Training Squadron; 2036th Communications Squadron (AFCC); 513th Field Training Det (ATC); Det 22, 40th Aerospace Rescue & Recovery Squadron (MAC); OLAF, 4444th Operations Squadron; Det 2, USAF Fighter Weapons School; Det 3, Tactical Air Warfare Center; Air Force Office of Special Investigation Det 2007; Det 454, Air Force Audit Agency; Det 11, 4400th Management Engineering Squadron; Det 18, 25th Weather Squadron

Operational aircraft:
366th Tactical Fighter Wing
F-111A   389th TFTS   (MO)
          391st TFTS
EF-111A   390th ECS

Below: A pair of EF-111A electronic jammers of the 390th ECS, Mountain Home AFB

Myrtle Beach

Myrtle Beach AFB
South Carolina 29579–5000
USA

Command:
Tactical Air Command

Phone:
(803) 238–7211

Autovon:
748–1110

Area located:
Southern edge of Myrtle Beach, off Highway 17 south

Date est:
1956 (served as an army air base between 1941 and 1947)

Named after:
The city of Myrtle Beach

Acreage:
3,793

Personnel:
3,500 military personnel, 760 civilians

Units:
354th Tactical Fighter Wing; 353rd Tactical Fighter Squadron, 355th Tactical Fighter Squadron, 356th Tactical Fighter Squadron; 2066th Communications Squadron (AFCC); Det 11, 39th Aerospace Rescue and Recovery Squadron (MAC); 301st Field Training Det (ATC); 1816th Reserve Advisor Squadron; Det 3, 3rd Weather Squadron; Det 12, 440th Management Engineering Squadron (ATC); Det 2105, Air Force Office of Special Investigations; 73rd Tactical Control Flight (TAC)

Operational aircraft:
345th Tactical Fighter Wing (TAC)
A-10A   353rd TFS   (MB)
              355th TFS
              356th TFS
CH/HH-3E
              Det 11, 39th ARRS

Notes:
The base shares the runway with Myrtle Beach Jetport. The 354th Tactical Fighter Wing's mission is to provide the capability to deploy worldwide and to be able to provide close air support

Left: In a crisis, A-10As from Myrtle Beach could be deployed to reinforce overseas assets, such as this Suwon, Korea, based A-10A

Nellis

Nellis AFB
Nevada 89191–5000
USA

Phone:
(702) 652–1800

Autovon:
682–1800

Area located:
12.8 km (8 miles) northeast of Las Vegas situated off I-15

Command:
Tactical Air Command

Date est:
July 1941

Named after:
1st Lt William H. Nellis, a P-47 pilot killed over Europe on 27 December 1944

Acreage:
11,274 plus ranges totalling 3,014,566 acres

Personnel:
10,260 military personnel, 1,200 civilians

Units:
Tactical Fighter Weapons Center; 57th Fighter Weapons Wing, USAF Air Demonstration Squadron (Thunderbirds); USAF Fighter Weapons School; Deputy Commander for Adversary Tactics; Deputy Commander Civil Engineers; Deputy Commander Resources Mangement; Deputy Commander Tactics and Test; 4513th Adversary Threat Training Group; 4440th Tactical Fighter Training Group (Red Flag); 554th Operations Support Wing; 554th Range Group; 554th Medical Group; 37th Tactical Fighter Wing; 820th Civil Engineering Squadron "Red Horse"; 3096th Aviation Depot Squadron; 2069th Communications Group

Operational aircraft:
37th Tactical Fighter Wing (TAC)
F-4E8G   561st TFS
        562nd TFS
        563rd TFS
57th Fighter Weapons Wing (TAC)
A-10A   (WA)
F-15C/D

Right: (Top to bottom) an A-10A, an F-15C, an F-111D and an F-16C overfly the Hoover Dam

F-16/A/B/C
F-111/D/F
F-16A 64th Aggressor Squadron
     65th Aggressor Squadron
     37th Tactical Fighter Wing
T/AT-38
 F-117
Air Demonstration Squadron (TAC)
     (The Thunderbirds)
F-16A/B

Notes:

Established as an Army Air Corps gunnery school in 1941, Nellis has become the home of the Tactical Fighter Weapons Center which sets out to provide the nearest thing to real war most fighter jocks will hopefully ever meet. See Tonopah Test Range Airfield for details on the F-117 Stealth Fighter, operated by the 37th Tactical Fighter Wing. (The F-117 have been operated out of Tonopah which is located deep within one of the base's ranges)

Below: Seymour Johnson AFB's 336th TFS, 4th TFW, was the first unit to receive the two-seat, all-weather F-15E strike fighter

Peterson

Peterson AFB
Colorado 80914–5000
USA

Command:
Air Force Space Command

Date est:
1942

Named after:
1st Lt Edward J. Peterson, who was killed in a crash at the base in 1942

Acreage:
1,155

Personnel:
6,040 (active duty) military personnel, 1,204 (reserves), 2,651 civilians

Units:
HQ Air Force Space Command; HQ North American Aerospace Defense Command; HQ US Space Command; HQ NORAD; NORAD Cheyenne Mountain Complex; 1st Space Wing; 3rd Space Support Wing; 302nd Tactical Airlift Wing (AFRES); 2nd Space Wing

Operational aircraft:
731st Tactical Airlift Squadron (AFRES)
C-130B

Notes:
The 2nd Space Wing is located 14.5 km (9 miles) away at Falcon AFB. Peterson AFB is one of America's most prized possessions. It is the heart of a global network of radars and satellites which constantly supply information to safeguard the free world's boundaries

Seymour Johnson

Seymour Johnson AFB
North Carolina 27531–5000
USA

Phone:
(919) 736–5400

Autovon:
488–1110

Command:
Tactical Air Command

Date est:
June 1942

Named after:
Lt Seymour A. Johnson, a navy pilot killed in an aircrash in 1941

Acreage:
3,320

Personnel:
5,100 military personnel, 800 civilians

Units:
4th Tactical Fighter Wing, 334th Tactical Fighter Squadron, 335th Tactical Fighter Squadron, 336th Tactical Fighter Squadron; 68th Air Refueling Wing (SAC), 911th Air Refueling Squadron; 2012th

Communications Squadron (AFCC); OLAD, 191st Fighter Interceptor Gp (Michigan ANG), 916th Air Refueling Gp (AFRES)

Operational aircraft:
4th Tactical Fighter Wing (TAC)
F-4E   334th TFS
            335th TFS
            336th TFS
68th Air Refueling Group (SAC)
KC-10A   911th ARS

Notes:
The 336th TFS was the first operational unit to receive the F-15E, completing its conversion from the F-4E in October 1989. The wing will eventually receive 72 F-15Es as the Air Force continues its long-range interdiction capabilities. The F-4Es will be transferred to the Air National Guard and Air Force Reserve units and one squadron of F-15Es may transfer to USAFE

Shaw

Shaw AFB
South Carolina 29152–5000
USA

Command:
Tactical Air Command

Phone:
(803) 668–8110

Autovon:
965–1110

Date est:
August 1941

Named after:
2nd Lt Ervin D. Shaw, one of the first Americans to see action in France during World War I. His Bristol fighter was shot down in 1918 while on reconnaissance

Acreage:
3,363 plus 8,078 leased acres at the Poinsett Bombing Range southwest of Sumter

Personnel:
5,232 military personnel, 510 civilians

Units:
HQ 9th Air Force (TAC); 363rd Tactical Fighter Wing, 16th Tactical Reconnaissance Squadron, 17th Tactical Fighter Squadron, 19th Tactical Fighter Squadron, 33rd Tactical Fighter Squadron; 507th Tactical Air Control Wing, 21st Tactical Air Support Squadron

Below left: An F-16C of the 363rd TFW, Shaw AFB

Below right: A 363rd TFW pilot about to depart in his F-16

Operational aircraft:
363rd Tactical Fighter Wing (TAC)
RF-4C   16th TRS
F-16C/D   17th TFS
            19th TFS
            33rd TFS
507th Tactical Air Command Wing
OT-37B   21st TASS   (SR)

Tinker

Tinker AB
Oklahoma 73145–5900
USA

Phone:
(405) 732–7321

Autovon:
884–4360

Command:
Air Force Logistics Command

Date est:
March 1941

Named after:
Maj Gen Clarence L. Tinker whose LB-30 crashed as he led a bombing mission during World War II

Acreage:
4,790

Personnel:
7,355 military personnel, 510 civilians

Units:
HQ Oklahoma City Air Logistics Center; Engineering Installations Div (AFCC); 3rd Combat Communications Gp (AFCC); 28th Air Division (TAC); 552nd Airborne Warning & Control Wing (TAC), 964th Airborne Warning and Control Squadron (AW&CS), 965th Airborne Warning and Control Squadron, 966th Airborne Warning and Control Squadron; 8th Tactical Deployment Control Squadron, 507th Tactical Fighter Gp (AFRES)

Operational aircraft:
465th Tactical Fighter Squadron (AFRES)
F-4D   (SH)
8th Tactical Deployment Control Squadron (TAC)
EC-135K
552nd Airborne Warning & Control Wing (TAC)
E-3A/B/C 964th AW&CS
             965th AW&CS
             966th AW&CS
C-135E: this aircraft is operated on behalf of the 1st Space Wing

Notes:
The Logistics Center provides logistics support for bombers, electronics, instruments and jet engines

Tonopah

Tonopah Test Range Airfield
Nellis AFB
Nevada 89191-5000
USA

Phone:
see Nellis AFB

Autovon:
see Nellis AFB

Command:
Tactical Air Force

Area located:
To the northwest of Nellis AFB,

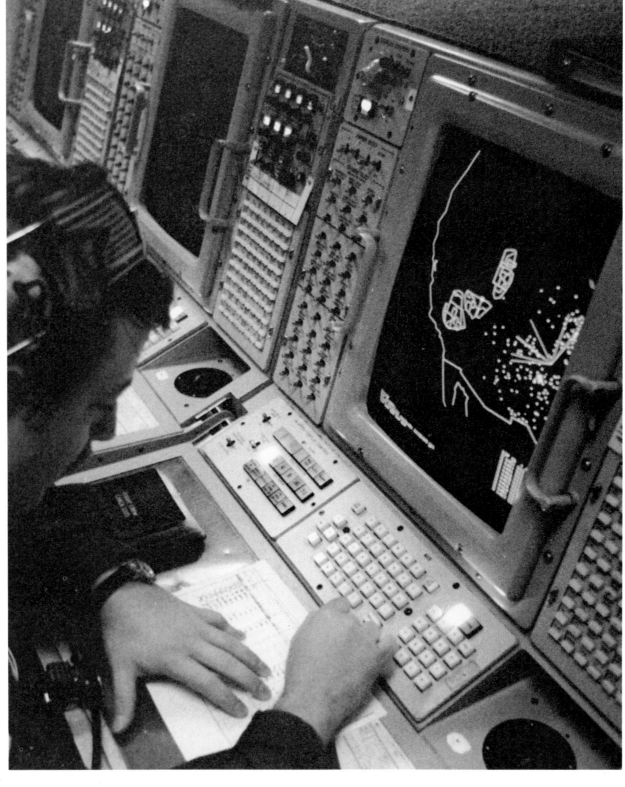

within the overall Nellis area. It is *totally* closed to visitors

Date est:
1980

Personnel:
2,650

Units:
37th Tactical Fighter Wing

Operational aircraft:
37th Tactical Fighter Wing
F-117A   415th TFS

          416th TFS
          417th TFTS
T/AT-38   417th TFTS

Notes:
Lying within the overall confines of Nellis ranges, Tonopah Test Range Airfield became home to the 4450th Tactical Group (TG) in 1980. The secret location has always been off limits to everyone not involved in the F-117A project. The TG was first equipped with A-7Ds as trainers and the first F-117 arrived at the site in 1982, initial operational capability

Above: This tactical controller's multi-mode display enables him to readily direct friendly aircraft from his airborne station aboard a 552nd AWCW Boeing E-3

was achieved in 1983. In October 1989, the 4450th TG was redesignated as the 37th TFW under the operational command of the Twelfth Air Force. Most personnel involved with the wing live in the greater Las Vegas area and are flown in each day by commercial contract aircraft

Tyndall

Tyndall AFB
Florida 32403–5000
USA

Phone:
(904) 283–1113

Autovon:
523–1113

Command:
Tactical Air Command

Date est:
December 1941

Named after:
1st Lt Frank B. Tyndall, a World War I pilot who was killed in 1930 flying a P-1

Acreage:
29,115

Personnel:
4,623 military personnel, 1,695 civilians

Units:
Air Defense Weapons Center; 325th Tactical Training Wing, 1st Tactical Fighter Training Squadron, 2nd Tactical Fighter Training Squadron; 475th Weapons Evaluation Gp; 325th Combat Support Gp; Southeast Air Defense Sector; HQ Air Force Engineering and Services Center (SOA); 3625th Technical Training Squadron (ATC); 2021st Communications Squadron (AFCC); 4702nd Computer Services Squadron (TAC); Det 1, 48th Fighter Interceptor Squadron (TAC); TAC NCO Academy East

Operational aircraft:
325th Tactical Training Wing (TAC)
F-15A/B   1st TFTS   (TY)
           2nd TFTS

Notes:
The Air Defense Weapons Center provides the DoD with a central location for operational and technical support on all matters relating to air defense. It also provides management services for all home based aerial target operations. Home of the William Tell Fighter Weapons Meet

Right: Succor for the tireless vigil; a Boeing E-3 replenishes its fuel tanks from a Boeing KC-135A

Aircraft

(The aircraft listed under Units in this section include all aircraft operated by regular AF, ANG and AFRES units)

A-7D/K Corsair II

(information for the A-7D)

Contractor:
LTV Aerospace and Defense Company (formerly Vought Corporation)

Status:
Operational

Powerplant:
One Allison TF41-A-1 non-afterburning turbofan engine, 6,577 kg (14,500 lb) thrust

Accommodation:
Pilot only

Dimensions:
Span 11.81 m (38 ft 9 in)
Length 14.06 m (46 ft 1.5 in)
Height 4.9 m (16 ft 0.75 in)

Weights:
Empty 8,973 kg (19,781 lb)
Gross 19,051.2 kg (42,000 lb)

Performance:
Max speed at S/L 1,123 km/h (698 mph)
Ferry range with external tanks 4,620 km (2,871 miles)

Armament:
Fixed: one M61A1 20 mm (0.79 in) multibarrel gun
Disposable: up to 6,804 kg (15,000 lb) of air-to-air or air-to-surface missiles, bombs, Gator mines, rockets or gun pods on six underwing and two fuselage attachments

Notes:
The A-7 has had a successful life, entering service with the Navy in 1966 as a lightweight attack aircraft. In October 1966 the Air Force ordered a tactical attack version powered by a 6,464 kg (14,250 lb) thrust Allison/Rolls-Royce TF41-A-1 (derivative of the RR Spey) turbofan. It first flew on 26 September 1968 and the first aircraft were accepted by the Air Force in December 1968. The A-7 equipped a substantial number of USAF TAC wings. Today it is in service with the ANG but is becoming increasingly vulnerable to emerging counter-air threats and has major logistics problems. To combat these problems the A-7 Upgrade (A-7 Plus) Program will provide the Air Force with a Close Air Support/Battlefield Air Interdiction which would support the Army's AirLand battle concept into the 1990's and beyond. In May 1987 Congress authorized LTV Aerospace to build two prototype aircraft

Below: The re-worked LTV YA-7F is now capable of achieving supersonic speed in level flight

Right: LTV's A-7D, affectionately known to its pilots and groundcrew as "SLUF," signifying "Short Little Ugly Feller"

Units:
107th TFS (MI); 112th TFS (OH); 120th TFS (CO); 124th TFS (IA); 146th TFS (PT); 149th TFS; 152nd TFTS (AZ); 162nd TFS (OH); 166th TFS (OH); 174th TFS (HA); 175th TFS (SD); 188th TFS; 198th TFS; 4450th TG (LV)

Service number:
380+

A-10
Thunderbolt II

Contractor:
Fairchild Republic Company, a division of Fairchild Industries

Status:
Operational

Powerplant:
Two General Electric TF34-GE-100 turbofan engines; each approx 4,111 kg (9,065 lb) thrust

Accommodation:
Pilot only

Dimensions:
Span 17.53 m (57 ft 6 in)
Length 16.26 m (53 ft 4 in)
Height 4.47 m (14 ft 8 in)

Weights:
Empty 11,321 kg (24,959 lb)
Max gross 22,680 kg (50,000 lb)

Performance:
Combat speed at S/L, clean, 706 km/h (439 mph)
Range with 4,309 kg (9,500 lb) of weapons and 1.7 hr loiter, 20 min reserve, 463 km (288 miles)

Armament:
Fixed: single 30 mm (1.18 in) GAU-8/A gun
Disposable: eight underwing hard points and three underfuselage for up to 7,258 kg (16,000 lb) of ordnance, including various types of free-fall or guided bombs, combined effects munition (CEM) dispensers, gun pods, or six AGM-65 Maverick missiles, and jammer pods. Chaff and flares carried internally to counter radar or infrared-directed threats. The centerline pylon and the two flanking fuselage pylons cannot be occupied simultaneously. AIM-9L Sidewinder AAM dual rail adapters, to allow four missiles to be carried in pairs

Notes:
The A-10 came about because of an Air Force requirement for a specialist battlefield close air support (CAS) aircraft to replace its mix of aircraft types that had been adapted

to support the ground forces. The Air Force looked at many designs between 1963 and 1969 without finding any aircraft that could meet the task. In 1970, the Air Force asked Northrop and Fairchild to build two prototype aircraft each, under the new Department of Defense "fly before buy" policy. The Air Force planners were looking for an aircraft that met four basic requirements: combat effectiveness, survivability, simplicity and responsiveness. Fairchild won the contract two years later in January 1973 over the Northrop designed A-9. The A-10 was built around the huge General Electric Gatling gun which is 6.7 m (22 ft) in length. With the GAU-8/A Avenger 30 mm (1.18 in) seven-barrel gun able to fire 2,100 or 4,200 rds/min, the A-10 is designed to tackle armored vehicles in the Close Air Support role. It is itself heavily armored and its systems are duplicated, making it possible for it to carry on flying even with one engine, half the tail and other equipment shot away or damaged. Its Pave Penny pod provides the capability to fly both day and night missions and its laser target-designation offers extremely accurate targeting. It is in service with regular, AFRES and ANG units. The Air Force is now looking at aircraft to replace the A-10 during the late 1990's, and a version of the F-16 seems to be the favorite for its successor

---

Units:

23rd TFW, 74th TFS, 75th TFS, 76th TFS (EL); 45th TFS; 46th TFTS (BD); 47th TFS (BD); 51st TFW, 25th TFS; 104th TFS (MD); 118th TFS (CT); 131st TFS (MA); 138th TFS (NY); 176th TFS (WI); 303rd TFS (KC); 343rd TFW, 18th TFS (AK); 345th TFW, 353rd TFS, 355th TFS, 356th TFS (MB); 355th TTW, 333rd TFTS, 357th TFTS, 358th TFTS (DM); 81st TFW, 92nd TFS, 509th TFS, 510th TFS, 511th TFS (WR); 706th TFS (NO)

Service number:
650+

Below: Fairchild Republic's tank-killing A-10A Thunderbolt II

B-57 Night Intruder

Contractor:
Martin Co; licensed from English
Electric Aviation, UK

Status:
Retired

Powerplant:
(A, B, C, E, G) two 3,265 kg
(7,200 lb) thrust Wright J65-W-5
(US Sapphire) turbojets; (D) two
4,990 kg (11,000 lb) Pratt & Whitney
J57-37A two-shaft turbojets

Accommodation:
Two crew

Dimensions:
Span (A, B, C, E, G) 19.5 m
(64 ft)
Length (A, B, C, E) 19.96 m
(65 ft 6 in); (G) 20.42 m (67 ft)
Height (A, B, C, E, G) 4.75 m
(15 ft 7 in)

Weights:
Empty (A, B, C, E) 12,200 kg
(26,800 lb); (G) approx 12,700 kg
(28,000 lb)
Maximum (A) 23,133 kg (51,000 lb);
(B, C, E, G) 24,950 kg (55,000 lb)

Performance:
Maximum speed (A, B, C, E, G)
937 km/h (582 mph)
Service ceiling (A, B, C, E, D)
14,630 m (48,000 ft)
Maximum range with combat load
(A, B, C, E, G) 3,380 km (2,100 miles)

Armament:
(A and all RB versions) none; (B, C,
E, G) provision for four 20 mm
(0.79 in) or eight 12.7 mm (0.5 in)
fitted in outer wings, underwing
racks for two 226.8 kg (500 lb)
bombs or other stores, internal load
of 2,268 kg (5,000 lb) of bombs or
rockets

Notes:
The new Air Force at the end of the
1940's had a requirement for a light
tactical bomber, and a number of
American manufacturers put forward proposals, including the Martin Company. In October 1949 they
flew their trijet attack bomber, but it
was not a flexible enough design
and the aircraft was not taken up.
However the Air Force saw good
potential in the company and they
suggested that they should build a
foreign designed aircraft. The Martin B-57 was to be the first foreign
designed aircraft to be built in
America for any US military service
since 1918. The aircraft in question
was the English Electric Canberra
which, on 21 February 1951, became
the first jet aircraft to fly the Atlantic
without refueling, and at the same
time set a new transatlantic crossing
record. The flight was to signal the
licensing agreement to build the aircraft in America.
Martin built eight pre-production
aircraft, designated B-57A, while
they established their production
line and incorporated a number of
modifications to the British design.
They were fitted with Wright
J65-W-1 (license-built Armstrong

Sidley Sapphire) engines. The first
aircraft was flown on 20 July 1953.
The next batch to come off the
production line were 67 RB-57As
which had cameras installed behind
the bomb bay. The first unit to receive the aircraft in early 1954 was
the 363rd Tactical Reconnaissance
Wing at Shaw AFB.
The RB-57s were followed by the
B-57B Night Intruder which contained several major alterations, the
most obvious being the tandem
cockpit design. Internally a rotary
bomb launcher was fitted. The
B-57B was first flown on 28 June
1954, and a total of 202 were built.
The 461st Bombardment Wing
(TAC) was the first unit to receive

Above: Its English Electric Canberra
ancestry shows clearly in this in-flight
study of an RB-57A

the B-57B, with the first aircraft arriving on 5 January 1955. The 345th
Bombardment Wing followed in
1956 and then the 3rd Wing Pacific
Air Forces. At the same time a number of B-57C entered service in the
training role. The B-57B only had a
short life with TAC which ended in
1959. A number of aircraft were
handed over to the Air National
Guard in 1961 and 26 went to the
Pakistan Air Force

Below: A preserved example of Martin's
RB-57A

E-3B/C Sentry (AWACS)

Contractor:
Boeing Aerospace Company

Status:
Operational

Powerplant:
Four Pratt & Whitney TF33-PW-100/100A turbofan engines, 9,526 kg (21,000 lb) thrust each

Accommodation:
Basic operational crew of 20, including 16 AWACS mission specialists

Dimensions:
Span 44.42 m (145 ft 9 in)
Length 46.61 m (152 ft 11 in)
Height 12.73 m (41 ft 9 in)

Weights:
Gross 147,420 kg (325,000 lb)

Performance:
Max speed 850 km/h (530 mph)
Service ceiling above 8,840 m (29,000 ft), endurance six hours on station 1,600 km (1,000 miles) from base

Armament:
none

Notes:
The Air Force first proposed a requirement for an Airborne Warning and Control System (AWACS) aircraft in 1963. They were to be used to alert its air defense forces of approaching Soviet bomber forces, because ground-based radars were not capable of over-the-horizon monitoring. Once the enemy had been sighted the AWACS system would control all responses. The Tactical Air Command requirement was for an airborne surveillance platform and command center for TAC aircraft, while the Aerospace Command requirement was a "hard to find" command and control center.

On 23 July 1970, Boeing received a contract to supply two prototypes, designated EC-137D, based on the Boeing 707-320B. They flew comparative tests using prototype downward-looking surveillance radars built by Hughes Aircraft Company and Westinghouse Electric Corporation. On 5 October 1972 the Air Force announced that Westinghouse had won the radar contract for the E-3A, and the first production aircraft entered service

with the 552nd Airborne Warning and Control Wing at Tinker AFB on 24 March 1977.

Today the E-3 provides tactical commanders with real-time battle management information in support of tactical air operations. Over the years it has gone through a number of changes. Ten E-3As are being upgraded to the E-3C configuration by the addition of five more consoles and extra communications systems.

Twenty-four other E-3As are being upgraded to E-3B standard by the upgrading of communications equipment, which includes Joint Tactical Information Distribution System (JTIDS) and fitting extra consoles. Chaff/flare dispensers can now be fitted. In use also with NATO, both the United Kingdom and France have taken delivery of their first E-3s and the system will see service well into the 21st century

Above: The E-3A's radar can detect targets over 320 km (200 miles) away

Units:
552nd AW&CW, 963rd AW&CS, 964th AW&CS, 966th AW&CS

Service number:
34

Below: The E-3A is a derivative of the Boeing 707–320 jetliner

EB-66

Above: The sleek Douglas B-66B Destroyer

Contractor:
Douglas Aircraft Co
(now McDonnell Douglas)

Status:
Retired

Powerplant:
Two 4,536 kg thrust Allison J71-13
single shaft turbojets

Accommodation:
Crew of 2 or 4

Dimensions:
Span 22.1 m (72 ft 6 in)
Length 22.9–24 m (75 ft 2 in–
78 ft 9 in)
Height 7.16 m (23 ft 6 in)

Weights:
Empty average configuration
19,218 kg (42,369 lb)
Maximum 37,648 kg (82,000 lb)

Performance:
Maximum speed 982 km/h
(610 mph)
Service ceiling 13,100 m (43,000 ft)
Ferry range 3,220 km (2,000 miles)

Armament:
None

Notes:
Developed from the Navy A-3 Skywarrior, Douglas produced the B-66 Destroyer and the electronic reconnaissance EB-66. Although very similar externally to the Navy A-3, the Air Force version was a radically different airframe. A total of 72 B-66Bs were built but were not liked and were expensive to maintain. The platform did prove useful as a reconnaissance aircraft and the RB-66B entered squadron service in March 1956. A total of 145 RB-66B reconnaissance, 36 RB-66C electronic reconnaissance (four-man crew) and 36 WB-66D aircraft were produced. The platforms underwent a number of special mission upgrades. The EB-66 version served in Vietnam throughout the war and was later replaced in the electronic warfare role by the Grumman EF-111 Raven

Left: The first RB-66A with landing gear extended

EC-121
Warning Star

Contractor:
Lockheed California

Status:
Retired

Powerplant:
Four 3,250 hp Wright R-3350-91 Turbo-Compound 18-cylinder radials

Accommodation:
Varies between seven and 28 depending on mission and variant

Dimensions:
Span over wing tip tanks 38.45m (126 ft 2 in)
Length most variants 35.41m (116 ft 2 in)
Height most variants 7.52 m (24 ft 8 in)

Weights:
Empty most variants 36,564 kg (80,611 lb)
Maximum loaded 65,770 kg (145,000 lb)

Below: A Lockheed EC-121R, over South East Asia in January 1969

Performance:
Maximum speed at altitude 517 km/h (321 mph)
Service ceiling 6,279 m (20,600 ft)
Range 7,400 km (4,600 miles); endurance limit 20 hours

Armament:
None

Notes:
Following on from the military versions of the Constellation and Super Constellation, Lockheed started to deliver complete electronic warfare aircraft in 1953. Designated RC-121C, they were operated by Air Defense Command. Then re-designated EC-121C and other variants, they were put in service with the Aerospace Defense Command. The EC-121 was developed under the "Big Eye" program to act as an airborne warning and control platform for ADC interceptors. They saw service in Vietnam where their main duties were electronic reconnaissance, early warning, and as airborne mobile relay platforms for the Igloo White system which monitored air dropped beacons relaying information on enemy movements. The EC-121 in its many guises was used for almost every type of electronic mission being continually upgraded as new systems came along

Main picture: EF-111A, serial number 66–041, seen after delivery to the 366th TFW

Inset: A frontal aspect on the "Electric Fox," as the EF-111A is referred to by its crews

EF-111A Raven

Contractor:
Grumman Aerospace Corporation

Status:
Operational

Powerplant:
Two Pratt & Whitney TF30-P-3 turbofan engines, each 83,900 kg (18,500 lb) thrust with afterburn

Accommodation:
Crew of two, side-by-side in escape module

Dimensions:
Span spread 19.2 m (63 ft)
Fully swept 9.7 m (31 ft 10 in)
Length 23.16 m (76 ft)
Height 6.1 m (20 ft)

Weights:
Empty 25,072 kg (55,275 lb)
Gross 40,347 kg (88,948 lb)

Performance:
Max combat speed 2,216 km/h (1,377 mph)
Service ceiling with afterburn at combat weight 13,700 m (45,000 ft)
Combat radius with reserves 370–1,495 km (230–929 miles), according to mission

Armament:
None

Notes:
The EF-111 was developed by Grumman Aerospace from the General Dynamics F-111 using mostly off-the-shelf components. It was first deployed to RAF Upper Heyford in February 1984. The ALQ-99E is a development of the Navy's ALQ-99 which was used in the EA-6B. The ALQ-99E is itself now undergoing further modification. The ALQ-99E Tactical Jamming System is designed to deny enemy command and control units the necessary range, azimuth and altitude information used to guide their interceptors, SAMs and anti-aircraft artillery. The success of the Raven was proved during the raid on Libya when it cut an electronic sanitized path through the Libyan defenses for the F-111 bombers

Units:
346th TFW, 390th ECS; 42nd ECS

Service number:
42

F-4 Phantom II

(information for F-4E)

Contractor:
McDonnell Aircraft Company, a division of McDonnell Douglas Corporation

Status:
Operational

Powerplant:
Two General Electric J79-GE-17A turbojets, each 8,120 kg (17,900 lb) thrust with afterburning

Accommodation:
Pilot and weapon systems operator

Dimensions:
Span 11.6 m (38 ft 0.5 in)
Length 19.2 m (63 ft)
Height 4.9 m (16 ft 1 in)

Weights:
Empty 13,757 kg (30,328 lb)
Gross 20,030 kg (61,795 lb)

Performance:
Max speed at 12,700 m (40,000 ft)
Mach 2.0 class
Range with typical tactical load
1,126 km (700 miles)

Armament:
Fixed: one 20 mm (0.79 in) M61A1 multibarrel gun
Disposable: provision for up to four AIM-7E Sparrow, AGM-45A Shrike, AGM-88A HARM, or AIM-9 Sidewinder missiles on four underfuselage and four underwing mountings, or up to 7,257 kg (16,000 lb) external stores

Notes:
The F-4 first entered Air Force service in 1964, following trials in 1961 of the Navy's F-4B which was flown in comparison against the Air Force's fighters and won on all counts. This resulted in the Air Force ordering the F-4C for 16 of TAC's 23 Air Wings. The RF-4, equipped with a camera, radar and IR linescan, followed into service in 1965. The F-4C was followed by the D model which featured a APQ-100 radar instead of the APQ-109, and inertial navigation, plus a number of other improvements. This too was followed into service by the E model which had slatted wings, an internal gun and a more powerful engine.

For many years the work horse of the tactical air commands, the F-4 still has a major task in the Wild Weasel role. The F-4G is still the only dedicated defense suppression aircraft that at this time can employ both the HARM and the Shrike missiles. With its APR-38 Radar Attack

and Warning System, the F-4G can detect, identify and accurately locate, engage and destroy hostile radars. The APR-38 Product Upgrade Program (PUP) will update the warning/location Wild Weasel System to handle the advanced threat radars it may encounter in the 1990's.

The PUP upgrade is divided into two sections: Phase I increases the on-board computer memory and processing speed while Phase II extends the frequency range. Phase I achieved an Initial Operational Capability (IOC) in July 1988. Following problems with the first Phase II receiver prototype during FY 1987, the second part of the program is being extended to tackle the problems.

As the F-4E is replaced in regular units by the F-15 and F-16, it is being transferred to the ANG. The RF-4 provides a vital photo reconnaissance platform equipping two air wings

Below: An F-4E's APQ-120 fire control radar gets a thorough check out

Below: The end of another F-4E mission as the crew deplane

Above: The crew of this F-4G practice operating in an NBC warfare environment
Below: An Osan, Korea, based F-4E of the 51st TFW

Below: A German-based F-4C deploys its braking 'chute

Above: A 36th TFS F-4E headed for the wild blue yonder

Units:

F-4C

160th TFS; 199th FIS (the F-4Cs are due to be replaced by F-15A/B) (HF); 113th TFS (HF); 114th TFTS; 196th TFS F-4C/E; 123rd FIS

F-4D

121st TFS (DC); 704th TFS (TX); 170th TFS (SI); 457th TFS (TH); 179th FIS (AL); 179th FIS; 184th TFS; 111th FIS; F-4C/D; 194th FIS; 178th FIS; 27th TFW, 307th TFS, 113th TFS; 127th TFS; 177th TFTS; 136th FIS; 171st FIS (MI); 465th TFS (SH); 172nd TASS; 89th TFS (DO)

F-4E/G

163rd TFS (FW); 3rd TFS; 90th TFS F-4E/G (PN); 35th TTW, 20th TFTS, 21st TFTS (GA); 37th TFW, F-4E&G, 561st TFS, 562nd TFS, 563rd TFS (WW); 37th TFW, F-4E&G; 110th TAS (SL); 141st TFS (NJ); 347th TFW, 68th TFS, (the wing is converting to the F-18s); 4th TFW, 334th TFS, 335th TFS, 336th TFS; 51st TFW, 36th TFS (OS), 497th TFS (GU)

RF-4C

10th TRW, 1st TRS (AR); 26th TRW RF-4C (ZR)

F-5E/F Tiger II

(information for the F-5E)

Contractor:
Northrop Corporation, Aircraft Division

Status:
Retired

Powerplant:
Two General Electric J-85-GE-21B turbojet engines; each 2,268 kg (5,000 lb) thrust with afterburning

Accommodation:
Pilot only (two in tandem in F-5F)

Dimensions:
Span 8.13 m (26 ft 8 in)
Length 14.45 m (47 ft 4.75 in);
15.65 m (51 ft 4 in) (F-5F)
Height 4.07 m (13 ft 4.25 in); 4.01 m (13 ft 2 in) (F-5F)

Weights:
Empty 4,410 kg (9,721 lb)
Gross 11, 214 kg (24,722 lb)

Performance:
Maximum speed 1,705 km/h (1,060 mph)
Service ceiling 16,460 m (54,000 ft)
Range with max fuel, with reserve fuel for 20 min: 3,175 km (1,973 miles)

Armament:
Fixed: two M39-A2 20 mm (0.79 in) cannon in nose, with 280 rounds per gun (one 20 mm in F-5F) Disposable: two AIM-9 Sidewinder missiles on wingtip launchers; up to 3,175 kg (7,000 lb) or mixed ordnance on four underwing attachments and one underfuselage station. Optional armament and equipment includes AGM-65 Maverick, laser-guided bombs, and centerline multiple ejector rack

Notes:
Following the Korean War, fighter pilots (both Air Force and Navy) were asking for a lightweight, highly maneuverable aircraft, and in 1955 Northrop began work on a light-weight fighter. The Navy quickly pulled out but the Air Force ordered the new T-38 Talon for its trainer requirements. Northrop continued working on the design as a private program, and with some support from the Department of Defense it became a good seller to the international market. Deliveries started in 1972 and the two-seater followed in 1975. The Air Force saw this simple airframe as a perfect aircraft for its new dissimilar air combat training and took delivery of the aircraft, but in Soviet markings. Anyone who has flown a Red Flag exercise knows the F-5 flown by the Aggressors of the 57th FWW or their counterparts in Europe, the 10th TRW Aggressors from Alconbury, Great Britain. As of

end 1989 the F-5 has been withdrawn from service. It had been planned that the F-16 would be used as a replacement aircraft for dissimilar training but owing to cutbacks in funding all Aggressor squadrons have now been disbanded.

Main picture: Aggressor F-5Es lift-off for dissimilar fighter tactics training

Right: Aggressor F-5Es mimic Soviet practice, including their overall appearance

Below left: Northrop's first F-5F two-seater in unfamiliar Aggressor colors

Below right: The first F-5F, seen here in its original livery

F-15 Eagle

(information for the F-15C)

Contractor:
McDonnell Aircraft Company, a division of McDonnell Douglas Corporation

Status:
Operational

Powerplant:
Two Pratt & Whitney F100-PW-100 turbofan engines, each approx 10,800 kg (23,830 lb) thrust. Improved F100-PW-220 will equip new F-15s

Accommodation:
Pilot only

Dimensions:
Span 13.05 m (42 ft 9.75 in)
Length 19.45 m (63 ft 9.75 in)
Height 5.63 m (18 ft 5.5 in)

Weights:
Empty 12,383 kg (27,300 lb)
Gross 30,845 kg (68,000 lb)

Performance:
Max speed Mach 2.5
Service ceiling 18,288 m (60,000 ft)
Ferry range, with external fuel tanks, more than 4,632 km (2,878 miles); with conformal fuel tanks (CFTs), 5,745 km (3,570 miles)

Armament:
Fixed: one internally mounted M61A1 20 mm (0.79 in) multibarrel cannon; Disposable: four AIM-9L/M Sidewinder and four AIM-7F/M Sparrow air-to-air missiles, or eight AMRAAMs, carried externally. Provision for carrying up to 10,705 kg (23,600 lb) of ordnance on weapon stations

Notes:
The F-15 first flew 27 July 1972 and the first aircraft entered service in November 1974 and was accepted into squadron service in January 1976. Considered by many to be the finest fighter in the world, the F-15 is the Air Force's front-line fighter. It was designed to combat the new generation of Soviet combat aircraft that were expected to enter service during the late 1960's and early 1970's. Throughout the 1960's the Air Force had considered a number of design projects without any real idea what they would have to face in possible combat. And then the Soviets revealed a large range of new

aircraft at the Domodedovo airfield near Moscow in 1967. Three aircraft which caught the Air Force's eye were the MiG-23 variable-geometry fighter, the MiG-25 and the Su-15. The following year USAF requested three companies to produce designs for a single-seat air-superiority fighter. McDonnell Douglas, Fairchild and North American all competed for the order and in December 1968, three months after the commission of studies, McDonnell Douglas was announced the clear winner.

The first flight of the new aircraft was in July 1972, it entered service in November 1974, and the first F-15 squadron became operational in 1976. An early export buyer of the F-15 was Israel, and the F-15 first went into combat against Syrian MiG-21s in June 1979 over Lebanon. The Syrians lost several aircraft while the Israelis suffered no casualties.

Unlike the Navy's F-14s which have a crew of two, the F-15 was designed as a single-seater. In order to make life simple for the pilot the aircraft is highly automated; he has only to look at one main display, the head-up display. The F-15A and the two-seater trainer F-15B were followed by the F-15C and D in June 1979. The new aircraft could carry 907 kg (2,000 lb) of additional internal fuel and could be fitted with conformal fuel tanks. Starting in February 1983, the F-15s have been undergoing a MultiStage Improvement Program (MSIP). These improvements include a Programmable Armament Control Set (PACS), improved main computer, expanded Tactical Electronic Warfare System (TEWS) which provides improvements to the ALR-56C radar warning receiver, and the ALQ-135 countermeasures suite. MSIP aircraft are cleared for the AMRAAM missile, and the system for the AIM-7 and AIM-9 missiles have been upgraded. The first MSIP-equipped aircraft were delivered in June 1985.

The F-15E, the latest in the F-15 family, provides a long-range, large payload capability to strike second echelon targets at night and in any weather conditions while retaining a superior air-to-air capability. Although the F-15E has shorter range than the F-111 while carrying a similar load – 11,113 kg (24,500 lbs), it is capable of carrying a much wider mix of air-to-surface munitions. It is equipped with the Low Altitude Navigation and Targeting Infrared System for Night (LANTIRN) and the beyond visual

range Advanced Medium Range Air-to-Air Missile (AMRAAM). The F-15E entered IOC in mid-1989. The existing F-15s are being upgraded to increase their air superiority while the earlier F-15A/Bs are being transferred to Reserve units. The first ANG unit to receive the F-15 was the 159th TFG in 1985.

In Fiscal Year 1988 the Air Force received 42 F-15Es, bringing the total up to 92 aircraft. They have requested another 36 F-15 aircraft in FY 1989 with a total delivery number of 392 aircraft.

Units:
F-15A/B
5th FIS; 21st TFW, 43rd TFS (AK); 48th FIS; 49th TFW, 7th TFS, 8th TFS, 9th TFS; 318th FIS; 325th TTW, 1st TFTS, 2nd TFTS (TY); 405th TTW, 426th TFTS
F-15C/D
1st TFW, 27th TFS, 71st TFS, 94th TFS (FF); 32nd TFS (CR); 33rd TFW, 58th TFS, 59th TFS, 60th TFS (EG); 36th TFW, 22nd TFS, 53rd TFS, 525th TFS (BT); 18th TFW, 12th TRS, 44th TRS, 67th TRS (ZZ); 57th FIS (IS); 57th FWW (WA); 405th TTW, 426th TFTS, 555th TFTS

Service number:
A total of 1,266 airframes. Delivery in progress

Below: Condensation trails from its wing tips as this F-15 breaks to the left

Above: A two-seat F-15B over some typically hostile Aleutian terrain

Above: Two F-15As in "mirror image"

Below: An F-15C carrying AIM-7s and AIM-9s

Above: An F-15A undergoing maintenance at Robins AFB

Below: The instrument panel of an F-15C

Right: This F-15A cruises serenely, framed against a "street" of cumulus cloud

Below: An Elmendorf-based F-15D of the 21st TFW

F-16 Fighting Falcon

(information for the F-16C)

Contractor:
General Dynamics Corporation

Status:
Operational

Powerplant:
One Pratt & Whitney F100-PW-200(3) turbofan engine; approximately 11,340 kg (25,000 lb) thrust with afterburning. General Electric F110-GE-100 and Pratt & Whitney F100-PW-220 augmented turbofans will be alternative standard engines in future production aircraft

Accommodation:
Pilot only

Dimensions:
Span over missiles 10 m (32 ft 10 in)
Length overall 15 m (49 ft 3 in)
Height 5.09 m (16 ft 8.5 in)

Weights:
Empty 7,618 kg (16,794 lb)
Gross with external loads 17,010 kg (37,500 lb)

Left: This F-16C carries both AIM-120 (inboard) and AIM-9 (wingtips) missiles

Performance:
Max speed Mach 2 class
Service ceiling more than 15,240 m (50,000 ft)
Ferry range more than 3,200 km (2,000 miles)

Armament:
Fixed: one M61A1 20 mm (0.79 in) multibarrel cannon, with 500 rounds, mounted in fuselage Disposable: wingtip-mounted sidewinder missiles; seven other external stores stations for fuel tanks and air-to-air and air-to-surface munitions.

Notes:
First flown on 20 January 1974, the F-16 started life as a technology demonstrator to explore the possibility of a fighter that was cheaper and much smaller than the McDonnel Douglas F-15. There was no intention that the Lightweight Fighter Program would lead to production, but would provide answers for the next generation of aircraft. Both General Dynamics and Northrop competed in the trials, and at the same time it became clear that some of NATO's member countries were interested in a new aircraft to replace their F-104Gs. And so the program was revised in April 1974 as the Air Combat Fighter program. By December of the same year, the Air

Below left: A Korean-based F-16C of the 8th TFW

Force decided to purchase an initial 650 of the winning aircraft designed by General Dynamics, and in June 1975 the four NATO countries Belgium, Holland, Denmark and Norway also voted in favor.

With its exceptional air-to-air performance and a potent air-to-surface capability, the F-16 is the major tactical aircraft in the Air Force inventory and is replacing the much older F-4 in both the regular and reserve fleets. The first unit to receive the F-16 in January 1979 was the 388th Tactical Fighter Wing based at Hill AFB, Utah. Production of the F-16A and B came to an end in 1985, following delivery of the new F-16C and D which began in July 1984. A total of 27 regular air wings, plus four Air Force Reserve Wings and nine Air National Guard Wings, had received the F-16 by the end of FY 1988. The AMRAAM integration program is well under way and certification for the High-speed Anti-Radiation Missile (HARM) and Shrike Missile is progressing. Integration of these systems on the newest F-16 C/D block 40 aircraft was tested in FY 1989. The F-16 is also undergoing a pre-planned product improvement for its electronic countermeasures system. The F-16 Agile Falcon (MSIP IV) program is looking into ways to further develop the derivative F-16s in the 1990's and beyond, and it is a front runner in the replacement of the Fairchild A-10 in the Close Air Support role. A total of 1,562 F-16s of all types had been received by the Air Force at the end of FY 1989

Units:
F-16A/B
8th TFW, 35th TFS, 80th TFS; 56th TTW, 61st TFTS, 62nd TFTS, 63rd TFTS, 72nd TFTS (MC); 57th FWW F-16A/B/C/D (WA); 58th TTW, 310th TFTS, 311 TFTS F-16A/B, 312th TFTS, 314th TFTS F-16C/D (LF); 134th TFS; 157th TFS (SC); 159th FIS; 161st TFTS: 182nd TFS (SA); 195th TFTS; 347th TFW, 69th TFS, 70th TFS (MY); 388th TFW, 4th TFS, 34th TFS, 421st TFS (HL); 401st TFW, 612th AFS, 613th AFS, 614th AFS (TJ); 466th TFS; Air Demonstration Squadron (The Thunderbirds)
F-16C/D
50th TFW, 10th TFS, 313th TFS, 496th TFS (HR); 86th TFW, 512th TFS, 526th TFS, 417th TFS (RS); 363rd TFW, 17th TFS, 19th TFS, 33rd TFS (SW); 432nd TFW, 13th TFS, 14th TFS (MF)

Service Number:
F-16A/B: 735 + , F-16C/D: Total required 1,936. Delivery in progress

---

Below left: A foursome of 388th TFW F-16As from Hill AFB

Right: F-16C, serial 87–230, seen during a pre-service delivery test flight

Below: This F-16C is seen releasing one of its flares, used to draw away heat-seeking missiles

F-80C Shooting Star

Contractor:
Lockheed

Status:
Retired

Powerplant:
One Allison J33-A-45 turbojet,
2,360 kg (5,200 lb) thrust with water
injection

Accommodation:
Pilot only

Dimensions:
Span 11.85 m (38 ft 10.5 in)
Length 10.52 m (34 ft 6 in)
Height 3.45 m (11 ft 4 in)

Weights:
Empty 3,741 kg (8,240 lb)

Performance:
Maximum speed at S/L 960 km/h
(600 mph)
Service ceiling 13,440 m (44,100 ft)
Range 2,165 km (1,345 miles)

Armament:
Six 12.7 mm (0.5 in) machine guns
plus two 454 kg (1,000 lb) bombs
plus eight unguided rockets

Notes:
The development of the F-80 began
with the arrival of the de Havilland
Goblin jet engine in America. Lockheed was contracted to design, build
and fly a fighter designated XP-80 in
May 1943. It became the first aircraft
ever to be built at the "Skunk
Works" in Burbank, California. The
contract allowed only 180 days to
complete production and in fact the
work was completed in only 143
days. Unfortunately, the designers
had not taken account of the im-
mense pressures developed by the
Goblin engine, and in trials the thin
inlet duct was destroyed and sucked
into the engine. De Havilland in England stripped the engine from their
own Vampire aircraft and sent it to
California. With a much strength-
ened inlet the XP-80 made its maiden
flight on 8 January 1944. In flight
tests the new aircraft attained a top
speed of 808 km/h (502 mph) at
6,360 m (20,850 ft) with the engine
producing 1,117 kg (2,460 lb) of
thrust.

At the same time, General Electric
was working on their new jet engine
which in tests was able to produce

1,814 kg (4,000 lb) thrust. They too
supplied an engine to Lockheed, and
on 10 June 1944, the second prototype, designated XP-80A, flew for
the first time with the General Electric engine. The aircraft, which had a
top speed of 898 km/h (558 mph),
went into production, and USAAF
had received 45 by the end of World
War II. Although two aircraft
operated in Italy they were never
involved in combat. Originally the
Army Air Force had planned to purchase 5,000 P-80s, but with the end
of the war this number was reduced.
In December 1945 they placed an

order for 677 P-80As to be powered
by Allison J33 engines and fitted
with wing tip tanks.

Work continued on the design of
the new aircraft. The last 240 had a
new design with much thinner
wings, an improved weapons load
and more powerful engines which
featured water-alcohol injection.
These last aircraft were designated
P-80B. Work continued on both the
engine and aircraft, and the F-80C

Below: A tight four-plane echelon of
F-80Cs of the Acrojets, precursors to
today's Thunderbirds

(the P designation had been changed
to F in 1948) entered service with the
J33-A-23 engine and additional
weapons.

The F-80C was used by the US Far
East Air Force during the Korean
War. The first jet-to-jet combat took
place on 8 November 1950 when four
F-80Cs of the 51st Fighter Interceptor Wing took on four MiG-15s,
destroying one of them. The arrival
of the F-84 and F-86 heralded the
retirement of the F-80 from regular
service, but large numbers were
transferred to Air National Guard
units

F-82E Twin Mustang

Contractor:
North American Aviation

Status
Retired

Powerplant:
Two 1,600 hp Allison V-1710-143/ 145

Accommodation:
Two

Dimensions:
Span 15.62 m (51 ft 3 in)
Length 12.93 m (42 ft 5 in)
Height 4.22 m (13 ft 10 in)

Weights:
Gross 11,593 kg (25,559 lb)

Performance:
Maximum speed 752 km/h (461 mph) at 6,400 m (21,000 ft)
Service ceiling 1,856 m (38,900 ft)
Range 3,600 km (2,240 miles)

Armament:
Six machine guns, 1,818 kg (4,000 lb) of bombs

Notes:
The F-82 was the last propeller-driven aircraft produced in any number for the Air Force. North American started development of a long-range escort fighter in January

Below: The F-82B "Betty Jo" that flew non-stop from Honolulu to New York. The B model served as a bug ranged bomber escort

Above: This F-82 is seen leading an F-80 (to its left), and an F-86 (following). The black paint scheme indicates it is a radar-equipped F-82F or G

1944, utilizing two P-51 fuselages joined by a new wing section.

Although they took to the air in early 1945, the end of the war in Europe caused a reappraisal of the project and only 20 of the initial order of 500 P-82Bs were completed. The aircraft was still a good platform and it was decided to adapt it to carry a radar pod slung between the two cockpits. These were designated the F-82C and D. More variants followed: the F-82E was a standard fighter escort while the F and G models were both night fighters.

A total of 250 aircraft were built, of which 225 were in use with the Air Defense Command by 1948. In 1950, most of the aircraft were withdrawn from ADC. When war broke out there was a total of 40 F-82s in the Far East Air Forces, assigned to both the Fifth and Twentieth Air Forces. From Japan they flew missions over Korea during the early part of the war. They had a good record and are credited with destroying 20 enemy aircraft. After the war they were relegated to secondary roles and in October 1953 were withdrawn from service completely

F-84 Thunderjet

(information for the F-84G)

Contractor:
Republic Aviation

Status:
Retired

Powerplant:
One Allison J35-A-29 turbojet,
2,540 kg (5,600 lb) thrust

Accommodation:
Pilot

Dimensions
Span 11.10 m (36 ft 5 in)
Length 11.61 m (38 ft 1 in)
Height 3.84 m (12 ft 7 in)

Weights:
Empty 5,033 kg (11,095 lb)
Gross 10,670 kg (23,525 lb)

Performance:
Maximum speed 1,001 km/h
(622 mph) at sea level

Service ceiling 12,340 m (40,500 ft)
Range 3,220 km (2,000 miles)

Armament:
Six 1.27 cm (0.5 in) machine guns;
two 453.6 kg (1,000 lb) bombs

Notes:
Alexander Kartveli at Republic, looking for a jet fighter that would have the same success as the P-47 Thunderbolt, started design work in 1944 and after a number of false starts came up with a simple straight-wing aircraft with a tapered body. It was to be built around a General Electric TG-180 turbojet. Early in 1945 the Army Air Force ordered three prototypes, designated XP-84, with an order for 400 production aircraft. The first flight of the XP-84 was on 28 February 1946, and the second prototype flew in August 1946. The second XP-84 established a new US national record of 983 km/h (611 mph) on 7 September 1946. The manufacture of 25 pre-production aircraft commenced at once with modifications being made the whole time. These first aircraft

were designated YP-84A. The P-84B was the first operational variant and flew in June 1947, entering squadron service soon afterwards. A total of 226 were built to this standard.

The P-84C which followed had a new electrical system and had modifications to the fuel and hydraulics systems. The C made its first flight in April 1948, and two months later, on 11 June, the Air Force changed the designation P (Pursuit) to F (Fighter). A total of 191 F-84Cs were built.

The design work started on the F-84D in November 1948, this variant incorporating a more powerful version of the J35 engine which provided an increase in speed up to 965 km/h (603 mph); the payload also increased by 300 kg (660 lb). It also had a thicker skin and a new fuel system which had a heating system. They were the first Thunderjets to be used in Korea. Although the straight winged F-84 suffered heavy losses to the swept wing MiG-15, it found success as "the best ground-support jet in the theatre."

The F-84E, of which 843 were

built, made its first flight on 18 May 1949. It had an extra 30 cm (12 in) added to the fuselage which provided more space in the cockpit. On 22 September 1950 an EF-84E became the first jet to fly the Atlantic non stop using air-to-air refueling.

The last of the straight wing series was the AF-84G which was ordered by Tactical Air Command as a fighter bomber capable of carrying a tactical nuclear bomb. The F-84G was the first single seat fighter bomber to carry tactical nuclear weapons. Deliveries started in January 1951 and a total of 3,025 F-84Gs were built with 1,936 aircraft going to Allied air forces. As well as having a J35 engine with a thrust of 2,540 kg (5,600 lb) it also was capable of in-flight refueling and had an automatic pilot.

Below: The upper planview of
F-84D-10-RE, serial 48–781

F-84F Thunderstreak

Contractor:
Republic Aviation

Status:
Retired

Powerplant:
One Wright J65 turbojet, 3,275 kg (7,200 lb) thrust

Accommodation:
Pilot

Dimensions:
Span 10.24 m (33 ft 7 in)
Length 13.23 m (43 ft 5 in)
Height 4.57 m (15 ft)

Weights:
Gross 6,259 kg (13,800 lb)

Performance:
Maximum speed 1,118 km/h (695 mph)
Service ceiling 14,020 m (46,000 ft)
Range 3,540 km (2,200 miles) with drop tanks

Armament:
Six 1.27 cm (0.5 in) machine guns

Notes:
By 1949, Alexander Kartveli realized that the F-84 in its straight wing form had reached the end of its development, and so he started on a new design which fitted a 45 degree swept wing. The prototype, designated the YF-96A, made its first flight on 22 November 1952, and deliveries started to the squadrons in 1954. The Air Force decided that as the aircraft was a derivative of the F-84 and not a new design, it should be designated F-84F and not F-89 as planned. A total of 2,711 aircraft were produced. The last Thunderstreak was retired from American service in 1972

Above: One of a batch of 49 F-84F-35s built by General Motors, Kansas

Below: An early batch F-84F, on a predelivery check-out flight

65

RF-84F Thunderflash

Contractor:
Republic Aviation

Status:
Retired

Powerplant:
One Wright J65-W-7 turbojet, 3,450 kg (7,800 lb)

Accommodation:
Pilot

Dimensions:
Span 10.24 m (33 ft 7 in)
Length 14.52 m (47 ft 7 in)
Height 4.57 m (15 ft)

Weights:
Loaded 12,700 kg (28,000 lb)

Performance:
Maximum speed 1,092 km/h (679 mph) at sea level
Service ceiling 14,020 m (46,000 ft)
Range 3,450 km (2,200 miles)

Armament:
Four 1.27 cm (0.5 in) machine guns

Notes:
In 1952 it was decided to produce a final F-84 reconnaissance variant, designated RF-84F. The prototype made its first flight in February 1953. The airframe had a modified nose and wing root which allowed the installation of cameras in the nose. A total of 715 were built, 386 going to NATO countries. Squadron deliveries commenced in March 1954. Twenty-five RF-84Fs were further modified to operate from B-36 bombers by the use of a retractable hook

F-86 Sabre

Contractor:
North American Aviation Inc

Status:
Retired

Powerplant:
One 2,710 kg (5,970 lb) J47-27 single-shaft turbojet (F-86F); one 4,064 kg (8,920 lb) GE J73-3E single shaft turbojet (F-86H)

Accommodation:
Pilot only

Below: A Korean-based F-86A, the first US fighter to meet the MiG15 on equal terms

Dimensions:
Span 11.93 m (39 ft 1.5 in) (most marks)
Length 11.43 m (37 ft 6 in) (most marks)
Height 4.49 m (14 ft 8.75 in) (most marks)

Weights:
Empty 5,045 kg (11,125 lb) (F-86F), 6,276 kg (13,836 lb) (F-86H)

Performance:
Maximum speed 1,091 km/h (678 mph) (F-86F), 1,113 km/h (692 mph)
Service ceiling (clean) 15,240 m (50,000 ft)

Above: A YRF-84F about to hook onto its parent Convair GRB-36F

Range with external tanks 1,368 km (850 miles)

Armament:
Internal six 1.27 cm (0.5 in) Colt-Browning M-3 with usual load of 267 rounds per gun plus two underwing hardpoints for two tanks or two weapons load of 450 kg (1,000 lb) each and eight rockets or two air-to-air missiles (F-86F); four 20 mm (0.79 in) M-3 guns with 150 rounds plus 544 kg (1,200 lb) nuclear bomb or 1,360 kg (3,000 lb) of external stores

Notes:
Designed during World War II, the Sabre first flew on 27 November 1946. Following major changes in the design from a straight wing configuration to a swept wing and tail configuration, the Army decided to go with the swept wing. The Navy carried on with a straight wing design and this entered service as the first jet to serve at sea. The Army's XP-86 broke speed records when it reached a speed of 618 mph with its Chevrolet-built GE TG-180 engine. When it received the new 2,268 kg (5,000 lb) thrust TG-190 (J47) in 1949, it reached a new world record of 1,080 km/h (671 mph). The new Air Force had an aircraft which, in service in Korea, was regularly a winner against the North Korean MiG-15s.

The F-86D interceptor introduced the system of gunless collision interception which was directed by the on-board radar and the autopilot. The F-86E interceptor entered production in December 1950 with a slatted wing and a powered "flying tail." The high point in the Air Force inventory came with the more powerful F-86H.

Although the F-86 had only been in service for a year when the war in Korea broke out, the Sabre Jet was quickly rushed to the Fifth Air Force. The first 19 arrived in Korea on 1 December 1950, and on 16 December they were first flown in anger, on the following day claiming their first MiG. Although the forward bases were overrun by the Chinese, they continued to operate from bases in Japan, from where they quickly regained control of the air.

To further restrict the Chinese, the Fifth Air Force flew Combat Air Patrol (CAP) missions to prevent the Chinese from operating from their bases in the Antung area. In six months this area, nicknamed "MiG Alley," saw 44 MiG-15s shot down and a further 77 damaged by the F-86s for the loss of only six American jets. The fact that so many MiGs survived – although damaged – was due largely to the fact that the machine gun was not powerful enough to do major damage to a fast jet unless it was hit in a vital area. This was answered in part by the F-86As being replaced by F-86Es and Fs which could carry eight High Velocity Aerial Rockets (HVAR). By the end of the conflict, F-86 pilots were credited with 792 MiGs shot down at the cost of 78 Sabres lost.

In total, for all customers, 9,502 Sabres were built for worldwide use; only the Huey helicopter has been built in larger numbers in the West since World War II

F-89D Scorpion

Contractor:
Northrop

Status:
Retired

Powerplant:
Two Allison J35-A-35 turbojets,
3,266 kg (7,200 lb) thrust each

Accommodation:
Two

Dimensions:
Span 18.18 m (59 ft 8 in)
Length 16.40 m (53 ft 10 in)
Height 5.36 m (17 ft 7 in)

Weights:
Maximum 19,160 kg (42,241 lb)

Performance:
Maximum speed 1,023 km/h
(636 mph) at 3,230 m (10,600 ft)
Service ceiling 14,995 m (49,200 ft)
Range 2,200 km (1,370 miles)

Armament:
52 70 mm (2.75 in) FFAR rockets in
wing tip pods

Notes:
The first two-seat all-weather fighter
conceived to enter service with the
USAF, the project was started by
Northrop in late 1945 as a replacement for the P-61 Black Widow. The
prototype XF-89 first flew in August
1948 and the first F-89A entered service in September 1950. Problems
with the airframe and engine meant
that only 48 F-89As and Bs were
built. The C had almost as many
problems, and a series of crashes in
1952 during flight testing caused the
program to be delayed by several
months. In the end 163 F-89Cs entered service.

With all the problems sorted out,
the F-89D entered service in January
1954 with ADC. It was armed with
missiles only, the first missiles to be
carried being the Hughes GAR-1
(later redesignated as AIM-4). These
Falcon missiles were supersonic and
guided by radar. In November 1956,
350 modified F-89Ds designated
F-89J entered service armed with the
Douglas MB-1 (later redesignated
AIR-2) Genie unguided nuclear
armed rockets. This missile was the
first nuclear-armed air-to-air missile;
it was first tested in a live firing on

Right: The sole YF-89D, converted from
F-89B, serial 49–2463

19 July 1957.

At the height of its service with the
ADC, in June 1958, there were 286
F-89Js in their inventory. With the
arrival of the century series Genie-
armed F-101 and F-106s, the ADC
transferred the F-89J over to the
ANG who carried on with the nuclear armed aircraft until 1968

F-94C Starfire

Contractor:
Lockheed

Powerplant:
One Pratt & Whitney J48-P-5
turbojet, 3,970 kg (8,750 lb) thrust

Accommodation:
Two

Dimensions:
Span 12.93 m (42 ft 5 in)
Length 13.56 m (44 ft 6 in)
Height 4.55 m (14 ft 11 in)

Weights:
Gross 10,977 kg (24,000 lb)

Performance:
Maximum speed 941 km/h
(585 mph) at 9,144 m (30,000 ft)
Service ceiling 15,670 m (51,400 ft)
Range 1,930 km (1,200 miles)

Armament:
48 70 mm (2.75 in) rockets

Notes:
Work on the F-94 started in 1949, the
prototype being a conversion of the
Lockheed T-33. It made its first flight
on 1 July 1949, and the Air Force
ordered 110 F-94A aircraft. The
F-94B which followed had modified
fuel tanks and equipment, and a
total of 357 were built.

The largest number of F-94s built
were of the F-94C type. This model
had a redesigned fuselage, wing and
tail. First flown in 1950, the F-94C
entered service the following year. It
had lost its machine guns in favor of
air-to-air rockets installed in the
nose and two wing housings. It was
used by ADC for the defense of
mainland America.

The F-94 saw service in Korea
from the end of 1951. Here the aircraft gained a good reputation both
for its ease of maintenance and the
ability to operate in both bad
weather and at night. Operating
from Suwon AB they escorted B-29
strikes against the North Koreans.
The Cs continued in service with
USAF units until 1959 and with the
ANG until 1960

F-100 Super Sabre

Contractor:
North American (Rockwell)

Status:
Retired

Powerplant:
One Pratt & Whitney J57 two-shaft
turbojet with afterburner. (Most of
Block A) 6,576 kg (14,500 lb) J57-7;
(late Block A, all mark C) 7,257 kg
(1,600 lb) J57-29); (mark D,F)
7,690 kg (16,950 lb) thrust with
afterburner

Accommodation:
F-100 pilot only; F-100F two seat
operational trainer

Dimensions:
Span early A models 11.15 m (36 ft
7 in); remainder 11.81 m (38 ft 9.5 in)
Length 15.09 m (49 ft 6 in)
Height early A models 4.06 m (13 ft
4 in); remainder 4.96 m (16 ft 3 in)

Weights:
Empty (early A models) 8,936 kg
(19,700 lb); C 9,276 kg (20,450 lb);
D 9,525 kg (21,000 lb); F 10,115 kg
(22,300 lb)
Maximum loaded (early A models)
13,578 kg (29,935 lb); C, D 15,800 kg
(34,832 lb); F two fuel tanks, no
weapons, 13,925 kg (30,700 lb)

Performance:
Maximum speed 1,390 km/h
(864 mph, Mach 1.31)
Service ceiling 13,720 m (45,000 ft)
Ferry range 2,415 km (1,500 miles)

Armament:
Four 20 mm (0.79 in) M-39E cannon
each with 200 rounds (F has two
M-39Es only); (A) pylons for two
tanks and four hard points for
1,814 kg (4,000 lb) ordnance; (C,D)
two tanks and six pylons for
3,402 kg (7,500 lb) ordnance; (F) two
tanks and 2,722 kg (6,000 lb)
ordnance

Notes:
Design work started in February
1949 and it made its first flight on 25
May 1953. In November 1954 the aircraft was grounded after the Air
Force had received 70 aircraft and
North American had built a further
108. A major problem was found in
the inertia coupling between the roll
and yaw axes which needed modification, and the wings and fins were
lengthened. The 479th Fighter-Day
Wing was the first wing to receive
the new fighter and initial operational capability was achieved in
September 1955. The A model, of
which the Air Force accepted 203,
was phased out of front-line service
in 1958 and placed in storage or
handed to the Air National Guard.
They re-entered TAC control during
the 1961 Berlin crisis, manned by
ANG units. And the following year
TAC re-acquired a number of the A
models after the ANG units had
been stood down. The end of the line
for the A came in 1970 when the last
operational aircraft was taken off
the inventory. The F-100C entered
service with TAC in April 1955,
when it became operational with the
450th Fighter-Day Squadron, but it
never really lived up to the original
specification. It was the F-100D
fighter bomber that produced the
goods, entering service with the
405th Fighter Bomber Wing in September 1956.

The F-100 was used to pioneer
global deployment by means of
probe/drogue refueling, allowing the
Air Force to operate far from its
home bases. In Vietnam they had
great success both in low level bombing and flying high cover protection

Above right: These F-100D were among
the first USAF aircraft to deploy to
Vietnam

Right and far right: Two views of the
two-seat F-100F of which 339 were built

Left: The first YF-94, sire to the several
hundred F-94As and Bs that were to
follow

Above left: An F-89J carrying AIM-4s

F-101F/TF Voodoo

Contractor:
McDonnell Aircraft Co
(a division of
McDonnell Douglas Corporation)

Status:
Retired

Below: An F-101B with braking 'chute deployed

Powerplant:
Two 6,800 kg (14,900 lb) Pratt &
Whitney J57 two-shaft turbojets
with afterburners

Accommodation:
(F-101F), single seat interceptor
(F-101 TF)
twin tandem dual control

Dimensions:
Span 12.09 m (39 ft 8 in)
Length 20.55 m (67 ft 4.75 in)
Height 5.49 m (18 ft)

Weights:
Empty 12,700 kg (28,00 lb),
maximum load, 21,180 kg (46,700 lb)

Performance:
Maximum speed 1,963 km/h
Service ceiling 15,850 m (52,000 ft)
Range on internal tanks 2,500 km
(1,550 mifles)

Armament:
Three Falcon AIM-4D air-to-air
missiles semi-submerged under
fuselage plus two AIR-2A Genie
nuclear air-to-air rockets

Above: Two F-101As flank an RAF
Bomber Command delta-winged Avro
Vulcan

Notes:
Developed from the XF-88 Voodoo
which first flew on 29 September
1954, the F-101 was designed as an
escort for Strategic Air Command.
From this design came the F-101B of
which 478 were built for the Air
Defense Command. Designated the
F-101F they carried less fuel which
allowed the installation of an MG-13
radar fire-control system

F-102A Delta Dagger

Contractor;
General Dynamics/Convair

Status:
Retired

Powerplant:
One 7,802 kg (17,200 lb) thrust Pratt & Whitney J57-23 two shaft afterburning turbojet

Accommodation:
Single seat interceptor (F), two side-by side (TF) trainer

Right: F-102As parked out in the open in Vietnam, while a technical sergeant helps build a temporary anti-blast pen

Below: An F-102A in camouflage

Dimensions:
Span 11.62 m (38 ft 1.5 in)
Length 20.85 m (68 ft 5 in) (F-102A),
19.32 m (63 ft 4.5 in) (TF-102A)
Height 6.45 m (21 ft 2 in) (F-102A),
6.27 m (20 ft 7 in) (TF-102A)

Weights:
Empty 8,630 kg (19,050 lb); loaded
12,564 kg (27,700 lb); maximum
14,288 kg (31,500 lb)

Performance:
Maximum speed 1,328 km/h
(825 mph)
Service ceiling 16,460 m (54,000 ft)
Range 2,172 km (1,350 miles)

Armament:
Air-to-air guided missiles in internal bay; typical load would contain three Hughes AIM-4E Falcon beam-riders with semi-active homing plus three Hughes AIM-4F with infra-red homing

Notes:
First flown on 24 October 1953 (YF-102), the YF-102A flew a year later on 20 December 1954. Convair had flown the world's first delta wing aircraft, the XF-92A, but in 1948 the project was cancelled. But when the Air Force issued a specification for an advanced all-weather interceptor to be equipped with the Hughes MX-1179 weapons system consisting of a MG-10 radar, computer and AIM-4 missiles, Convair was ready. The new aircraft, which was fatter and longer than the XF-92A, was accepted, and Convair built 875 of the fighter design and 63 of the subsonic trainer. It entered service with Air Defense Command's 327th Fighter-Interceptor Squadron based at George AFB in April 1956. They served with all the Air Force's tactical commands, playing a major role in the air war in Vietnam. They served in the region from March 1962 until they were withdrawn in December 1969, during which period only 15 aircraft were lost even though they had flown air defense missions and combat patrols in support of B-52 missions. At the height of their role in Vietnam, during 1967–68, a minimum of 14 F-102s were on five minute stand-by at any one time. The last of the regular air force craft were retired to service with the Air National Guard by 1974 and all had been withdrawn from service by 1978

F-104 Starfighter

Contractor:
Lockheed California

Status:
Retired

Powerplant:
One General Electric J79 single-shaft turbojet with afterburner; (F-104A) 6,713 kg (14,800 lb); (F-104C-D) J79-7A 7,165 kg (15,800 lb) thrust

Accommodation:
F-104 A-C single seat interceptor; F-104 B-D twin seat trainer

Dimensions:
Span 6.68 m (21 ft 11 in) without tip tanks
Length 16.69 m (54 ft 9 in)
Height 4.11 m (13 ft 6 in)

Weights:
Empty 6,387 kg (14,082 lb)
Gross 13,054 kg (28,779 lb)

Performance:
Maximum speed 2,330 km/h (1,450 mph, Mach 2.2)
Service ceiling 17,680 m (58,000 ft)
zoom ceiling over 27,400 m (90,000 ft)

Below: The serial 53–7786 identifies this machine as the first of the two prototype XF-104s

Maximum range with weapons 483 km (300 miles); range with four drop tanks (high altitude, subsonic) 2,220 km (1,380 miles)

Armament:
Centerline rack rated at 907 kg (2,000 lbs) and two underwing pylons rated at 454 kg (1,000 lb); additional points for air-to-air missiles on fuselage, under wings or on wing tips

Notes:
The Starfighter was developed by Clarence L. Johnson following talks with fighter pilots in Korea during 1951. They asked for an aircraft that was very quick and agile even if this meant other aspects had to suffer. The XF-104 first flew three years later, on 7 February 1954, and the production model had its first flight on 17 February 1956. The design was a radical one with almost no wing and its ejector fired downward.

The F-104A entered service with Air Defense Command in 1958, and the C version was used by TAC as a fighter bomber and was fitted with a refueling probe. Although no longer in service in America, the Italians still fly the F-104S which was developed jointly by Lockheed and Fiat (Aeritalia)

Above right: Four F-104Cs of TAC's 479th TFW, George AFB

Right: The underside of an F-104C in camouflage

F-105 Thunderchief

Contractor:
Republic Aviation (Fairchild Republic)

Status:
Retired

Powerplant:
One Pratt & Whitney J75 two-shaft afterburning turbojet; (B) 10,660 kg (23,500 lb) J75-5; (D, F, G) 11,113 kg (24,500 lb) J75-19W

Accommodation:
Pilot only; F-105F two seat operational trainer; F-105G two seat ECM

Dimensions:
Span 10.65 m (34 ft 11.25 in)
Length (B, D) 19.58 m (64 ft 3 in); (F, G) 21.21 m (69 ft 7.5 in)
Height (B, D) 5.99 m (19 ft 8 in); (F, G) 6.15 m (20 ft 2 in)

Weights:
Empty (D) 12,474 kg (27,500 lb); (F, G) 12,879 kg (28,393 lb)
Maximum loaded (B) 18,144 kg (40,000 lb); (D) 23,843 kg (52,546 lb); (F, G) 24,495 kg (54,000 lb)

Performance:
Maximum speed (B) 2,018 km/h (1,254 mph); 2,382 km/h (1,480 mph)
Service ceiling 15,850 m (52,000 ft)
Tactical radius with 7,597 kg (16,750 lb) munitions 370 km (230 miles)
Ferry range with maximum fuel, 3,846 km (2,390 miles)

Armament:
Internal: one 20 mm (0.79 in) M-61 gun with 1,029 rounds in left side of fuselage, internal bay for ordnance of 2,722 kg (6,000 lb)
External: five pylons for load of 2,722 kg (6,000 lb) missiles/bombs/ECM pods

Notes:
First flown on 22 October 1955, the F-105 followed a private design project codenamed the AP-63. The F-105 is the largest single seat, single engine aircraft ever built. It was designed to fly in all weather conditions, with very high speed and endurance, and to deliver both nuclear and conventional weapons. Seventy-five of the B variant were built for TAC, entering service with the 355th Tactical Fighter Squadron at Eglin AFB, Florida, in August 1958, but it was not until mid-1959 that the Air Force had a complete squadron. The F-105B was quickly followed by the more advanced D model with Nasarr monopulse radar and Doppler navigation. The F model, of which 143 were built, was a tandem seat version which had been lengthened and had both a full equipment fit and dual controls. Thirty model Fs were converted as electronic countermeasures (ECM) attack aircraft which operated in the Wild Weasel role armed with Shrike and ARM anti-radar missiles

Below: Pre-dawn maintenance on an F-105D in South East Asia

F-106A/B Delta Dart

Contractor:
General Dynamics/Convair

Status:
Retired

Powerplant:
One 11,130 kg (24,500 lb) thrust
Pratt & Whitney J75-17 two shaft
afterburning turbojet

Accommodation:
Single seat interceptor (F-106A),
two seat in tandem trainer (F-106B)

Dimensions:
Span 11.67 m (38 ft 3.5 in)
Length 21.55 m (70 ft 8 in)
Height 6.18 m (20 ft 3.25 in)

Weights:
Empty 10,725 kg (23,646 lb),
Maximum load 17,350 kg (38,250 lb)

Performance:
Maximum speed 2,455 km/h
(1,525 mph)
Service ceiling 17,375 m (57,000 ft)
Range, combat radius 966 km
(600 miles)

Armament:
One internal 20 mm (0.79 in) M-61
multi-barreled cannon; internal
weapons bay for air-to-air guided
missiles. Typical load one AIR-2A
and one AIR-2G Genie rockets plus
two each AIM-4E, 4F or 4G Falcons

Notes:
The F-106 was a direct follow on
from the F-102 and was originally
designated F-102B. The aerody-
namic prototype first flew on 26 December 1956 and deliveries started
in July 1959 to Aerospace Defense
Command squadrons. The 498th
Fighter Interceptor Squadron, based
at Geiger AFB, Washington, was the
first unit to receive the new aircraft,
and it reached initial operational
capability in October 1959. By using
the new supersonic Area Rule the
airframe was much cleaner than its
predecessor, and with its new engine, had a peak speed that was
twice as fast as the F-102.

The Hughes MA-1 fire control system linked into the SAGE (semi-
Automatic Ground Environment)
defense system. The pilot acted
purely as a flight manager while the
ground based system controlled the
attack phase.

By 1979, the Aerospace Defense
Command still retained six F-106
squadrons. The F-106 finally left
regular service when the 24th Air
Division traded in their F-106s, and
were withdrawn from the Air
National Guard in 1988. This mighty
aircraft, built in the 1950's, has provided sterling service in the defense
of the United States. The remaining
airframes will continue to serve the
Air Force as they are being converted into OF-106 aerial target
drones.

Above: Two generations of fighters, as
an F-106A leads an F-16

Left: The nose-in-the-air landing
attitude adopted by this F-106A was
typical of first generation deltas

F-111

Contractor:
General Dynamics Corporation

Status:
Operational

Powerplant:
F-111A/E: two Pratt & Whitney
TF30-P-3 turbofan engines; each
8,390 kg (18,500 lb) thrust with
afterburners. F-111D: two TF30-P-9
turbofan engines; each 8,890 kg
(19,600 lb) thrust with afterburners.
F-111F: two TF30-P-100 turbofan
engines; each approx 11,400 kg
(25,100 lb) thrust with afterburners

Accommodation:
Crew of two side-by-side in escape
module

Dimensions:
Span spread 19.2 m (63 ft)
Fully swept 9.74 m (31 ft 11.5 in)
Length 22.4 m (73 ft 6 in)
Height 5.22 m (17 ft 1.5 in)

Weights:
Empty 23,525 kg (47,500 lb)
Maximum load 45,360 kg
(100,000 lb)

Performance:
Max speed at S/L Mach 1.2
Max speed at altitude Mach 2.5
Service ceiling more than 18,000
(59,000 ft)
Range with max internal fuel more
than 4,700 km (2,925 miles)

Armament:
Fixed: none
Disposable: two nuclear bombs in
internal weapon bay; four
swiveling wing pylons carrying
total external load of up to
11,340 kg (25,000 lb) of bombs,
rockets, missiles, or fuel tanks

Notes:
Tactical Air Command issued a SOR
(Special Operational Requirement)
on 14 June 1960 for a strike aircraft
to replace the Republic F-105 Thun-
derchief. At the same time the Navy
also had a requirement to replace its
McDonnell Douglas F-4, and so the
Department of Defense decided that
the two requirements should be run
as one program called the Tactical
Fighter, Experimental (TFX). Designs by Boeing and a joint General
Dynamics/Grumman team were
then the front runners, with the Boeing design being favored by both the
Air Force and Navy. Robert McNa-
mara disagreed, considering the
Boeing design too technologically
advanced and the Navy and Air

Above: An impressive frontal view of a
TAC F-111D

Force variants too different, which
would cause problems in common-
ality of spares. Therefore he ignored
his advisors, and on 24 November
1962 placed a developmental contract with General Dynamics for 23
aircraft; 18 were to be the basic
F-111A for the Air Force and five
would be the F-111B design for the
Navy. The F-111B was not a success
and suffered from many problems
which resulted in the Navy cancel-
ing the program in July 1968. Only
five development and two production aircraft were built.

The F-111A suffered almost as
many problems following its first
flight on 21 December 1964, but it
entered production and 141 of the
model were built. Deliveries started

in October 1967 to the 474th TAW, based at Nellis AFB, Nevada. The 428th Tactical Air Squadron deployed six of its F-111A to Thailand for trials over Vietnam in early 1968. The trials were not a success and the unit lost half of its aircraft in just four weeks. The aircraft was grounded while modifications were made, including a redesigned engine air inlet. A further 94 aircraft were built incorporating an enlarged inlet and were designated F-111E.

The next variant to enter Air Force service was the F-111D, which had the more powerful TF30-P-9 engine and the Mark II avionics suite, including an AN/APQ-30 attack radar, digital computer, AN/AP-189 Doppler navigation and head-up displays for both crew stations. Although the new avionics looked good on paper they were both costly and problematic.

Work on the design continued and in May 1973 the F-111F – "The aircraft that the F-111 should have been from the beginning" – made its first flight. The F-111F combined the best from each of the other designs with a Mark IIB avionics suite. The world's first blind first-pass precision attack aircraft when it entered service in 1967, it is still the Air Force's only long-range, day and night interdiction fighter. This will change when the F-15E comes into full service. The F-111Fs of the 48th TFW at RAF Lakenheath carried out a retaliatory raid against Libya in April 1986. Fitted with the Pave Tack system which provides a day/night capability to acquire, track and designate ground targets for

laser, infrared and optically guided weapons, they were able to hit their targets accurately. To provide increased self-protection the ALR-62 radar warning receiver and the ALQ-94/137 self protection jammer system are to be replaced. The ALR-621 entered service in July 1989. The Air Force also intend to procure ALQ-131/184 jammer pods for the F-111 fleet. Developed by ASD's Dynamics Laboratory and built by Boeing Military Aircraft Company, the AFTI/F-111 is fitted with the Mission

Adaptive Wing. This advanced wing does not have conventional flaps, slats, ailerons or spoilers; instead, the wing changes its camber by using hydraulic actuators to alter the shape of the flexible composite skin.

Above and below: Complementary views of an F-111A; in both views the aircraft's wings are extended for optimum lift and fuel economy

Units:

20th TFW, F-111E, 55th TFS, 77th TFS, 79th TFS (UH); 27th TFW, F-111D, 522nd TFS, 523rd TFS, 524th TFS (CC); 57th FWW F-111D/F (WA); 48th TFW, F-111F, 492nd TFS, 493rd TFS, 494th TFS, 495th TFS (LN); 366th TFW, F-111A, 389th TFTS, 391st TFS (MO)

Right: Lockheed's unbeautiful F-117A is specifically shaped to minimize the machine's radar and infra-red signatures

F-117

Contractor:
Lockheed Corporation

Status:
Operational

Powerplant:
Two General Electric F404-GE-400 turbofans each rated at 4,899 kg (10,800 lb) without afterburners

Accommodation:
Pilot

Dimensions:
Span 13.21 m (43 ft 4 in)
Length 20.09 m (65 ft 11 in)
Height 3.78 m (12 ft 5 in)

Weights:
Empty 10,000 kg (22,050 lb)
Gross 15,000 kg (33,070 lb)

Performance:
Cruising speed at S/L 1,037 km/h (645 mph)
Combat radius 345–360 miles

Armaments:
Not known, stored internally

Notes:
It is believed that Lockheed first flew an XST (Experimental Stealth Technology) demonstrator in 1977. It is possible that a total of seven of these small aircraft were built for testing

and that two crashed. The operational F-117 was first flown in 1982. The F-117 is believed to offer minimal radar, infra-red, acoustic and visual signatures. This is produced by a blended wing-fuselage design. Canted fins cover the engine exhausts to aid in IR shielding and a special finish to the aircraft reduces its radar signature. Its sensors are all passive in operation and the aircraft has no electromagnetic emissions while in flight.

The existence of a stealth fighter has been known for several years but was only revealed by the Air Force on 10 November 1988. The fighter has been in service since October 1983. The announcement was given as the aircraft was due to start flying during daytime. Two aircraft each dropped a 907 kg (2,000 lb) bomb near (not on) an infantry barracks on 20 December 1989. It was admitted that F-117s had taken part in the invasion of Panama to hit precise targets and that the mission was a complete success.

Units:
37th TFW; 415th TFW; (Nightstalkers); 416th TFW (Ghost Riders); 417th TFTS (Bandits)

Service number:
52 delivered with a further 7 on order; these are due to be delivered by Fall 1990

Above and below: The F-117A's angularity is meant to refract, rather than reflect radar beams

Above right and below right: In-flight views of the F-117A. Note the long, thin engine exhaust slot

OA-37B Dragonfly

Contractor:
Cessna Aircraft Company

Status:
Operational

Left: A line-up of A-37As in South East Asia

Left: An OA-37B closes in on a KC-135 to take on fuel

Powerplant:
Two General Electric J85-GE-17A turbojet engines, each 1,290 kg (2,850 lb) thrust

Accommodation:
Two, side-by-side

Dimensions:
Span over tip tanks 10.93 m (35 ft 10.5 in)
Length excluding fuel probe 8.62 m (28 ft 3.25 in)
Height 2.71 m (8 ft 10.5 in)

Weights:
Empty 2,817 kg (6,211 lb)
Gross 6,350 kg (14,000 lb)

Performance:
Max speed at 4,875 m (16,000 ft) 816 km/h (507mph)
Service ceiling 12,730 m (41,765 ft)
Range with maximum payload, 1,860 kg (4,100 lb) including ordnance, 740 km (460 miles)

Armament:
Fixed: one GAU-2B/A 7.62 mm (0.3 in) Minigun installed in forward fuselage
Disposable: four pylons under each wing able to carry various combinations of rockets and bombs

Notes:
Developed as America's first jet trainer and designated the T-34A, it was equipped with two Continental J69 (license-built Turbomeca Marbore) 417 kg (920 lb) thrust engines. The T-37B followed when all surviving T-37As were re-engined with J69-25 engines with 465 kg (1,025 lb) thrust. Production of the T-37 ended in 1975 when in excess of 1,300 aircraft were delivered both to the US Air Force and 14 other air forces around the world.

The A-37 Counter Insurgency (COIN) aircraft began to be delivered in May 1967; these aircraft were converted T-37 trainers. Within a year one squadron stationed in Vietnam had flown 10,000 combat missions. Today the Dragonfly is used in both the COIN and Forward Air Control (FAC) roles

Units:
23rd TASS (NF); SAD; 103rd TASS (PA) 169th TASS (IL); 172nd TASS (BC)

Service number:
85 +

OV-10A Bronco

Contractor:
Rockwell International
Corporation, Aircraft Operations

Status:
Operational

Powerplant:
Two Garrett T76-G-416/417
turboprop engines; each 715 hp

Accommodation:
Two in tandem

Dimensions:
Span 12.19 m (40 ft)
Length 12.67 m (41 ft 7 in)
Height 4.62 m (15 ft 2 in)

Weights:
Empty 3,127 kg (6,893 lb)
Overload gross weight 6,552 kg
(14,444 lb)

Performance:
Max speed at S/L, without
weapons, 425 km/h (281 mph)
Service ceiling 7,315 m (24,000 ft)
Combat radius with max weapon
load, no loiter, 367 km
(228 miles)

Armament:
Fixed: four forward-firing M60C
7.62 mm (0.3 in) machine guns;
Disposable: four external weapon
attachment points under short
sponsons, for up to 1,000 kg
(2,204 lb) of rockets, bombs, etc.;
fifth point, capacity 540 kg
(1,190 lb), under center fuselage.
Provision for carrying one
Sidewinder missile on each wing
and, by use of a wing pylon kit,
various stores, including rocket and
flare pods and free-fall ordnance.
Maximum weapon load 1,630 kg
(3,600 lb)

Notes:
Built for counterinsurgency opera-
tions it is now used in the Forward
Air Control role

Units:
19th TASS (OS); 22nd TASS (WH);
27th TASS (VV); 549th TASS (FL)

Service number:
75 +

Right: An OV-10A of the 27th TASS
overflying George AFB

P-38 Lightning

Contractor:
Lockheed

Status
Retired

Powerplant:
Two 1,250 hp Allison V-1710-49/53

Accommodation:
One

Dimensions:
Span 15.85 m (52 ft)
Length 11.53 m (37 ft 10 in)
Height 3 m (9 ft 10 in)

Weights:
Empty 6,169 kg
(13,600 lb)
Maximum 9,070 kg
(20,000 lb)

Performance:
Maximum speed 558 km/h
(347 mph) at 1,520 m (5,000 ft)

Service ceiling 11,890 m (39,000 ft)
Maximum range 2,293 km
(1,425 miles)

Armament:
One 20 mm (0.79 in) Hispano
cannon and four 13 mm (0.5 in)
Browning machine-guns in the
nose; maximum bomb load 907 kg
(2,000 lb)

Notes;
Development had started on the P-38
in 1937. Designed as a long-range
tactical fighter, the XP-38 prototype
made its first flight on 27 January
1939. Production was delayed because of a belief that the new American bombers could defend them-
selves against attack. It became clear
that this would not be the case and
the Lightning began to operate in
Europe from mid-1942. It also
operated in the Pacific theater and is
credited with more Japanese aircraft
shot down than any other type. It
was withdrawn from service in 1949

P-47 Thunderbolt

Contractor:
Republic

Status:
Retired

Powerplant:
One 2,300 hp Pratt & Whitney
Double Wasp R-2800-59

Accommodation:
Pilot

Dimensions:
Span 12.43 m (40 ft 9.25 in)
Length 11.02 m (36 ft 1.75 in)
Height 3.86 m (12 ft 8 in)

Weights:
Empty 4,540 kg (10,000 lb)
Gross 6,630 kg (14,600 lb)

Performance:
Maximum speed 687 km/h

(427 mph)
Service ceiling 11,278 m (37,000 ft)
Maximum range 3,170 km
(1,970 miles)

Armament:
Eight fixed 13 mm (0.5 in) machine
guns in the wings; maximum bomb
load 907 kg (2,000 lb); six or eight
8 cm (3 in) rockets if required

Notes:
The Republic P-47 entered service in
1942. Designed as a strategic escort
for the B-17s and B-24s, it served
with distinction on every front. It
began operations in March 1943,
and between then and the end of the
war it is credited with the destruction of over 7,000 enemy aircraft
both on the ground and in the air. A
total of 15,686 aircraft were built
and it continued in service until 1955

Opposite: A fine color study of P-38E,
serial 41-2286

Above: A P-47D of the 307th FS, 31st
FG, operating over Europe

Below: The Thunderbolt's elliptical
wingform and wide track landing gear
are clearly visible in this view of a P-47D
somewhere in England

P-51 Mustang

Contractor:
North American

Status:
Retired

Powerplant:
One 1,510 hp Packard Merlin
V-1650-7

Accommodation:
Pilot

Dimensions:
Span 10.37 m (34 ft 0.25 in)
Length 9.85 m (32 ft 3.25 in)
Height 4.17 m (13 ft 8 in)

Weights:
Empty 7,125 lb (3,232 kg)
Maximum 5,262 kg (11,600 lb)

Performance:
Maximum speed 703 km/h
(437 mph)
Service ceiling 12,770 m (41,900 ft)
Maximum range 3,700 km
(2,300 miles)

Armament:
Six 13 mm (0.5 in) Browning
machine guns; maximum bomb
load 907kg (2,000 lb), or six 13 mm
(0.5 in) rockets

Notes:
Given 120 days to design and build a
new fighter, North American took up
the challenge and the prototype
made its first flight in October 1940.
The first production models went to
the RAF a year later where it gained
the name Mustang. It was obvious
that the engine was not capable enough and trials began with the Rolls
Royce Merlin. Flight tests began in
late 1942.

They entered service with the 8th
Air Force on 1 December 1943 and
flew their first mission on 13 December. By March 1944 they were
operating over Berlin. Goering
stated, "When I saw those Mustangs
over Berlin I knew the war was lost."
By the end of the war in Europe
P-51s equipped all but one of the 8th
Air Force fighter groups.

The Mustang underwent a number of major modifications during its
production run which numbered
over 14,000. It served in Korea and in
fact more F-51s flew in Korea than
the F-82

Above right: A P-51D of the 375th FS,
361st FG, in post-June 1944 European
paint scheme

P-61
Black Widow

Contractor:
Northrop

Status:
Retired

Powerplant:
Two 2,000 hp Pratt & Whitney
R-2800-65

Accommodation:
Three

Dimensions:
Span 20.12 m (66 ft)
Length 15.11 m (49 ft 7 in)
Height 4.47 m (14 ft 8 in)

Weights:
Empty 9,980 kg (22,000 lb)
Maximum 17,240 kg (38,000 lb)

Performance:
Maximum speed 589 km/h
(366 mph) at 6,096 m (20,000 ft)
Service ceiling 10,089 m (33,100 ft)
Maximum range 4,830 km
(3,000 miles)

Armament:
Four 13 mm (0.5 in) guns; four
726 kg (1,600 lb) bombs underwing

Notes:
Designed from the outset as a night
fighter, the P-61 was the USAAF's
standard night fighter by the end of
the war. Work started on the design
during 1940, with Northrop paying
particular attention to the European
experience of air combat. The Army
Air Force contracted Northrop in
March 1941 to build 13 YP-61s, and
followed with a further order for 410
six months later. By the time of the
first flight of the prototype in May
1942, the order had risen to over 600
aircraft. The first production aircraft
started to arrive with the squadrons
in late 1943. The early production
models featured a remotely controlled dorsal turret with four 13 mm
(0.5 in) machine guns, but they did
not prove successful and the later
aircraft appeared without them.

They first became operational in
the South Pacific in July 1944, and on
the first night of operations the
Black Widows destroyed four Japanese aircraft. The last version of the
P-61 was the F-15A Reporter.

Left: P-16C, America's first true night/
all-weather fighter

T-33

Contractor:
Lockheed

Status:
Retired

Powerplant:
One 2,360 kg (5,200 lb) Allison
J33-35 single-shaft turbofan

Accommodation:
Dual control pilot and student in
tandem

Dimensions:
Span 11.85 m (38 ft 10.5 in) without
wingtip tanks
Length 11.51 m (37 ft 9 in)
Height 3.56 m (11 ft 8 in)

Weights:
Empty 3,667 kg (8,081 lb)
Full 6,551 kg (14,442 lb)

Performance:
Maximum speed 950 km/h
(590 mph)
Service ceiling 14,480 m
(47,500 ft)
Maximum range 2,165 km (1,345
miles)

Armament:
Two 12.7 mm (0.5 in) M-3 machine
guns; provision for underwing
munitions

Notes:
The T-33 was a development of the
F-80 Shooting Star. It was nearly
three feet longer to allow a position
for the instructor. Lockheed produced 5,691 of all types including
the AT-33 close support attack train-

er and the RT-33 photo-reconnais-
sance trainer

Above: For years the T-33A served as
the advanced training workhorse

T-38A Talon and AT-38B

Contractor:
Northrop Corporation

Status:
Operational

Powerplant:
Two General Electric J85-GE-5 turbojet engines; each 1,210 kg (2,680 lb) thrust dry, 1,750 kg (3,850 lb) thrust with afterburners

Accommodation:
Student and instructor, in tandem

Dimensions:
Span 7.7 m (25 ft 3 in)
Length 14.14 m (46 ft 4.5 in)
Height 3.92 m (12 ft 10.5 in)

Weights:
Empty 3,250 kg (7,164 lb)
Gross 5,485 kg (12,093 lb)

Performance:
Maximum level speed at 11,000 m (36,000 ft) more than Mach 1.23, 1,300 km/h (812 mph)
Ceiling above 16,765 m (55,000 ft)
Range, with reserves, 1,760 km (1,093 miles)

Armament:
T-38A none
AT-38B practise bomb dispensers

Notes:
First flown in 1959, the Talon has proved an excellent twin seat jet trainer. It is used by ATC, SAC and TAC, and in its AT-38B configuration is fitted with a gunsight and practise bomb dispensers. The T-38 is being rewired to allow it to carry on into the next century.

Units:
475th TTW, 433rd TFTS, 434th TFTS, 435th TFTS, 436th TFTS, 12th FTW, 560th FTS; 14th FTW, 38th FTS; 47th FTW, 86th FTS; 71st FTW, 25th FTS; 80th FTW, 97th FTS, 3246th TW/AD

Above left: T-38A Talons of the Thunderbirds departing Nellis AFB

Left: America's first dedicated advanced trainer to have full supersonic performance was the Northrop T-38A

UH-1N Iroquois

Contractor:
Bell Helicopter Textron

Status:
Operational

Powerplant:
Pratt & Whitney Canada T400-CP-400 Turbo "Twin-Pac," consisting of two PT6 turboshaft engines coupled to a combining gearbox with a single output shaft; flat-rated to 1,290 shp

Accommodation:
Pilot and 14 passengers, or cargo, or external load of 1,800 kg (4,000 lb)

Dimensions:
Rotor diameter (with tracking tips)
14.89 m (48 ft 10.25 in)
Length of fuselage 12.92 m
(42 ft 4.75 in)
Height 4.53 m (14 ft 10.25 in)

Weights:
Gross mission weight 5,080 kg
(11,200 lb)

Performance:
Maximum cruising speed at S/L
185 km/h (115 mph)
Service ceiling 4,000 m (13,000 ft)
Maximum range, no reserves,
420 km (261 miles)

Armament: (optional)
Two General Electric 7.62 mm
(0.3 in) Miniguns or two 40 mm
(1.57 in) grenade launchers; two
seven-tube 2.75 cm (1.08 in)
rocket launchers

Notes:
Used in the combat rescue role, the

Above: TAC units use the UH-1N in both the utility transport and search and rescue mission roles

UH-1N is a twin engined variant of the UH-1

Units:
57th FWW; SAD; 37th ARRS, Det-8;
89th MAW; 67th ARRS; 1550th FTS;
304th ARRS; 475th ABW; 3246th
TW/AD

Missiles

AGM-45A Shrike

Contractor:
Naval Weapons Center

Status:
Operational

Powerplant:
Rocketdyne Mk 39 Mod 7 or
Aerojet Mk 53 solid-propellant
rocket motor

Guidance:
Texas Instruments passive homing
head

Warhead:
High-explosive fragmentation,
weighing 66 kg (145 lb)

Dimensions:
Length 3.05 m (10 ft)
Body diameter 20.3 cm (8 in)
Span 91.4 cm (3 ft)

Weights:
Launch weight (depending on sub
type) 180 kg (400 lb)

Performance:
(Estimated):
Range more than 5 km (3 miles)

Aircraft types:
F-4G/E, F-16C, F-105, EF-111

Notes:
A development of the Sparrow, the
AGM-45 began as a Navy project in
1961, receiving its AGM-45A designation in 1962. Production commenced the following year and it
underwent a number of quick
changes as new communist radars
were identified. It was used by both

the Navy and Air Force during the
Vietnam War and by the Israelis
during the Yom Kippur War.

A total of 12 versions of the supersonic Shrike missile were produced
for both the Navy and Air Force. The
Air Force received more than 13,000
missiles between 1965 and 1978. The
missile is being upgraded to improve
its capabilities at low levels

Below: An AGM-45 seen slung beneath
the F-105G Wild Weasel

AGM-65 Maverick

Contractor:
GM-Hughes, Missile Systems Group

Status:
Operational

Powerplant:
Thiokol TX-481 solid-propellant rocket motor

Guidance:
Self-homing electro-optical guidance system

Warhead:
High-explosive, shaped charge

Dimensions:
Length 2.49 m (8 ft 2 in)
Body diameter 30.5 cm (1 ft)
Wing span 72.0 cm (2 ft 4 in)

Weights:
Launch weight 210 kg (463 lb)

Performance:
Range of 1–22 km (0.6 to 14 miles)

Aircraft types:
A-7D, A-10, F-4D/E/G, F-5E/F, F-16, F-111 and F-117 (possible)

Notes:
Hughes won the battle to build the AGM-65 against competition from Rockwell in June 1968 and production commenced in 1971. The missile is designed for use against pinpoint targets such as tanks and columns of vehicles. The first batch of 17,000 was completed in 1975. Production has continued ever since at a reduced rate.

The first generation missiles are controlled by a TV camera mounted in the nose of the missile, the picture being shown on a screen in the cockpit. Once the missile is fired, its homing is controlled automatically. The missile was using during both the Vietnam and the 1973 Yom Kippur Wars with some success against ground targets.

The AGM-65B had a new head which provided Scene-Magnification: the pilot no longer needed to see the target, he could use the seeker's head to provide an enlarged image on his screen. This model was in production between May 1980 and May 1983. The AGM-65C Laser Maverick allowed either a ground spotter or another aircraft to illuminate the tar-

get with a laser beam which the missile would follow. The 65C was followed by the AGM-65E built for the Marine Corps with the Rockwell tri-Service seeker and a heavy blast-fragmentation warhead designed for use against heavy emplacements and fortifications.

The AGM-65D IR Maverick entered its engineering development stage in May 1977 with the Hughes

IIR tri-Service seeker. The imaging infra-red seeker allowed the missile to lock onto much longer ranges. It was more suited to the weather of Europe and could be fired at night. The AGM-65D is the standard missile for USAFE A-10s. Over 15,000 missiles of this type have been ordered by the Air Force.

The AGM-65G, first launched in 1987, has an IIR seeker and a

Above: This AGM-65 stands before an A-10A

35.17 kg (298 lb) blast fragmentation warhead. It is designed for use against large ground targets and ships. The AGM-65G has a digital autopilot and a pneumatic rather than hydraulic actuation system

AGM-78
Standard ARM

Contractor:
General Dynamics Pomona Division

Status:
Retired

Powerplant:
Aerojet (ATSC) Mk 27 Mod 4
boost/sustain solid motor

Guidance:
Radar homing

Warhead:
Conventional blast/fragmentation,
direct-action and proximity fuzes

Dimensions:
Length 4.57 m (15 ft)
Body diameter 34.3 cm (1 ft 1.5 in)
Wing span 1.09 m (3 ft 7 in)

Weights:
635 kg (1,400 lb)

Performance:
Speed Mach 2.5
Range up to 56 km (35 miles)

Aircraft types:
F-105F/G, F-4G

Notes:
In September 1966 the Naval Air Systems Command contracted General Dynamics, Pomona Division, to build an anti-radiation missile to replace the Shrike. The missile was to be a development of the Standard RIM-66A ship-to-air missile. Flight testing of the new missile started in 1967 and production of the AGM-78 Model commenced in late 1968. It entered service on the Air Force's F-105F and G Wild Weasel and the Navy's A-6B and E.

Early production models had used the T1 radiation seeker from the AGM-45 Shrike, but this was quickly replaced by a Maxson broad-band seeker for the main production run

Right: The full complement of defense-suppression missiles carried by the F-4G Wild Weasel (reading in descending order) comprises: AGM-88, AGM-65, AGM-78 and AGM-45. To make use of these missiles, the parent aircraft's fixed multi-barrel cannon has been removed to make room for a series of broad-band radio frequency analysers and associated electronics

AGM-88A
HARM

Contractor:
Texas Instruments Inc

Status:
Operational

Powerplant:
Thiokol smokeless dual-thrust solid-propellant rocket motor. Hercules second source

Guidance:
Passive homing guidance system, using seeker head that homes in on enemy radar emissions

Warhead:
High-explosive

Dimensions:
Length 4.17 m (13 ft 8 in)
Body diameter 24 cm (9.5 in)
Wing span 1.13 m (3 ft 8 in)

Weights:
366 kg (807 lb)

Performance:
Cruising speed supersonic, altitude limits S/L to 12,000 m (40,000 ft)
Range more than 16 km (10 miles)

Aircraft types:
A-7, A-10, F-4G, F-16, F-117 (possible)

Notes:
In 1972 the Naval Weapons Center began research for a new purpose-built air-launched ARM that would be capable against the new generation of Soviet radars. At the same time it provided funds for a number of industry studies. The new missile had to have a much higher speed, which would allow it to reach its target before the enemy operators could switch the radar off.

In 1974 Texas instruments were selected as the system integration contractor with a number of other companies building different parts.

The missile operates in three modes. In the first mode the missile's ALR-45 radar warning receiver identifies the threat, and the launch computer then takes control for the firing. In the second mode the seeker searches for targets of opportunity which the earlier Shrike and Standard missiles could not do. In the third mode the missile can be fired blind in the general direction of known targets. If the target remains silent the missile will self-destruct after its flight, if a radar starts up the missile will automatically home in.

The missile is carried by the F-4G Wild Weasel and is being integrated for use with the F-16. The Air Force hopes to buy a total of 9,273 missiles by the time the production run ends in 1994

AIM-4 Super Falcon

Contractor:
Hughes Aircraft Company

Status:
Retired

Powerplant:
Solid-propellant motor, some versions with boost/sustain

Guidance:
AIM/4A/E/F and AIM-26A/B: semi-active radar homing guidance; AIM-4C/D/G: infrared homing system; AIM-7A: semi-active homing/infrared terminal homing

Warhead:
AIM-26A: 1.5 kT nuclear; remainder: 13–18 kg (29–40 lb) high-explosive

Dimensions:
Length: AIM-4 1.97 m (6 ft 5.8 in); AIM-4A 1.98 m (6 ft 6 in); AIM-4B/C/D 2.02 m (6 ft 7.5 in); AIM-4E/F 2.18 m (7 ft 2 in); AIM-4G 2.06 m (6 ft 9 in); AIM-26A 2.14 m (7 ft); AIM-26B 2.07 m (6 ft 9.5 in); AIM-47A 3.2 m (10 ft 6 in)
Body diameter: AIM-4/4A/B/C/D 163 cm (6.4 in); AIM-4E/F/G 16.8 cm (6.6 in); AIM-26A 27.9 cm (11 in); AIM-26B 29 cm (11.4 in); AIM-47A 33.5 cm (1 ft 1 in)
Wing span: AIM-4/4A/B/C/D 50.8 cm (1 ft 8 in); AIM-4E/F/G 16.8 cm (6.6 in); AIM-26A 27.9 cm (11 in); AIM-26B 29 cm (11.4 in); AIM-47A 33.5 cm (1 ft 1 in)

Weights:
Launch weight: AIM-4 50 kg (110 lb); AIM-4A 54 kg (120 lb); AIM-4B 59 kg (130 lb); AIM-4C/D 61 kg (134 lb); AIM-4E/F 68 kg (150 lb); AIM-4G 66 kg (145 lb); AIM-26A 92 kg (203 lb); AIM-26B 119 kg (262 lb); AIM-47A 363 kg (800 lb)

Performance:
Speed: AIM-4 Mach 2.8; AIM-4A/B/C Mach 3; AIM-4D/E/F/G/H Mach 4; AIM-26A/B Mach 2; AIM-47A Mach 6
Max range: AIM-4 8 km (5 miles); AIM-4A/B/C/D 9.7 km (6 miles); AIM-4E/F/G 1.3 km (7 miles); AIM-26A 8 km (5 miles); AIM-47A 161 km (100 miles)

Aircraft types:
F-4, F-89H, F-101, F-102, F-106

Notes:
The Hughes Falcon was the world's first operational air-to-air missile. The Air Force asked for bids to build a radar based fire control system and a guided AAM for the new generation of jets that were starting to appear both in prototype form and still on the drawing boards of America's aircraft builders. It was not a requirement that the fire control system and missile should come from the same manufacturer but in the event Hughes Aircraft were given both projects. The following notes use the 1962 Air Force missile designations rather than the 1950 code to differentiate between the various missiles in the Falcon family.

The GAR-1 Falcon (AIM-4) was originally classed in 1947 as an experimental fighter (XF-98) under a project codenamed Dragonfly. The missile was powered by a single-charge Thiokol solid motor and was guided to the target by semi-active radar homing (SARH). Its receiver aerials positioned just behind the radome, steering was controlled by elevons on the trailing edges of the delta wings.

The F-89H and J carried three missiles in each of the two wing tip pods, and the F-102A carried six missiles in its weapons bay. Both aircraft entered IOC with the Air Defense Command in the middle of 1956. The first Infra-red seeker missile was the glass-nosed AIM-4B which entered service in 1957, followed by the SARH AIM-4A which had larger control planes well behind the wings.

The AIM-4C, which was almost 5 cm (2 in) longer than the original AIM-4, had an improved IR seeker which was able to lock onto targets against a wider range of background temperatures. Because the seeker locked onto its target as soon as the missile was launched it meant that the pilot was able to break off the attack for a new target.

The Super Falcon, the AIM-4E, entered service in 1958 arming the F-106A. This missile was upgraded in all departments; its guidance was controlled by an advanced SARH, it had longer wing root fillets and it carried a larger warhead. The 4F model, which followed in May 1959, was another SARH missile with improved guidance and improved ECCM. It also had a 102 mm (4 in) metal probe on the nose to improve the missile's aerodynamics. Within weeks the AGM-4G was introduced, combining the body of the 4F with a new IR seeker. The seeker provided better lock-on against smaller mis-

siles at much greater distances than before.

The missile was continually being improved. In 1960, another leap forward was made with the introduction of the much larger and more powerful AIM-26. This missile was able to provide high SSKP in head-on attacks, although its SARH was less precise. This resulted in the fitting of a similar nuclear warhead to the Genie. The AIM-26B was similar but was fitted with a conventional warhead. This model was the first to be used by other air forces and license-built by Saab-Scania as the RB 27.

As the speed of the jets increased so the speed of the missiles had to do likewise, and by 1958 the Air Force was considering a Mach 3.2 interceptor to be built by North American. The F-108 Rapier would have the Hughes ASG-18 radar which would provide mid-course guidance and target illumination at ranges in excess of 161 km (100 miles). It was

to be armed with the GAR-9 (AIM-47A) IR missile. Although the project fell by the wayside, the missile was used in the Lockheed YF-12A research interceptor, which was later to be developed into the SR-71 Blackbird.

In 1963 the last variant went into production, the AIM-4D, designed as a pure anti-fighter missile. It combined the small airframe of the early design with the 4G's IR seeker and engine. Thousands of the 4A and 4C were rebuilt to this configuration. And finally the 4D was further developed with the fitting of an Active Optical Proximity Fuze (AOPF) which utilized four laser beams to provide the optimum point to explode the missile. This project was killed off in 1971 because of lack of funds

Below: The AIM-4D heat-seeker

Right: AIM-7 Sparrow missiles mounted on this F-15A's lower fuselage

AIM-7 Sparrow

Contractor:
Raytheon Company/General
Dynamics Pomona Division

Status:
Operational

Powerplant:
AIM-7E: Aerojet or Rockwell Mk 52
mod 2 PB/AP solid motor;

AIM-7F, M: Hercules Mk 58 Mod 0
boost-sustain rocket motor

Guidance:
AIM-7A Radar beam riding;
AIM-7B Active radar homing;
AIM-7C/D/E/F/M Semi-active radar
homing

Warhead:
High-explosive, blast
fragmentation, (E) 30 kg (66 lb);
(F,M) 40 kg (88 lb); all with either

proximity or DA fuzes

Dimensions:
Length: AIM-7A 3.56 m (11 ft 8 in);
AIM-7B/C/D/E/F 3.66 m (12 ft);
AIM-7M 3.68 m (12 ft 1 in)
Body diameter: 20.3 cm (8 in)
Wing span: AIM-7A/B 0.99 m (3 ft
3 in); remainder 1.02 m (3 ft 4 in)

Weights:
Launch weight: AIM-7A 141 kg
(310 lb); AIM-7B 191 kg (420 lb);

AIM-7C 172 kg (380 lb); AIM-7D
200 kg (440 lb); AIM-7E 205 kg
(452 lb); (F,M) 228 kg (503 lb)

Performance:
Max speed more than Mach 3.5
Range: AIM-7E 22.5 km (14 miles);
AIM-7F more than 40 km (25 miles)

Aircraft types:
F-4, F-15, F-16 (ADF)

Notes:

The Sparrow is a missile system that has undergone many changes since Sperry Gyroscope started a Navy program codenamed Project Hot Shot in 1946. The first flight tests began in 1953. This early model, the AAM-N-2 Sparrow I, was guided to the target by the fighter's radar. It entered IOC with the Navy in July 1956. The year before, Douglas had suggested the Sparrow II as the main armament for its proposed F5D-1 Skylancer but the project was cancelled by the Navy in 1956. The Canadian Air Force decided to continue with the project but again the money ran out and it was finally abandoned in 1958.

The basic concept of the missile had caught the eye of Raytheon and it started work on a semi-active radar homing missile, the AIM-7C Sparrow III. It was powered by an Aerojet solid motor and entered service with the Navy in 1958. With the introduction of the AIM-7D in 1960 came the Air Force's first real interest in the family. The AIM-7D was procured for its F-4 Phantoms, which could carry four Sparrows recessed into the lower fuselage.

The AIM-7E used a Rocketdyne freestanding solid motor with Flexadyne propellant (Mk 38) which provided a slight increase in speed. Its warhead was designed to shatter into 2,600 steel fragments. The 7E also had two sub-types, the 7E-2 and 7E-3, that provided better maneuverability. It was followed into service in 1977 by the AIM-7F which had an all solid state guidance, allowing more space for a yet larger Hercules Mk 58 motor. The latest model, the AIM-7M, uses an inverse-processed digital monopulse seeker. Designed to improve performance at lower cost, it first appeared in 1983

Below: An AIM-7 powers away from an F-15A

AIM-9
Sidewinder

Contractor:
Raytheon Company/Ford
Aerospace

Status:
Operational

Powerplant:
Solid motor various suppliers

Guidance:
Solid-state infrared homing
guidance

Warhead:
High-explosive

Dimensions:
Length 2.87 m (9 ft 5 in)
Body diameter 12.7 cm (5 in)
Fin span 63.5 m (2 ft 1 in)

Weights:
Launch weight 86.6 kg (191 lb)

Performance:
Max speed above Mach 2

Aircraft types:
A-7, A-10, F-4, F-15, F-111

Notes:
The basic design for the Sidewinder is now over 40 years old, work having started on the design at what is now called the US Naval Weapons Center, China Lake, in the late 1940's. The first prototype was flown in 1953 and the missile entered service with both the US Navy and Air Force as the AIM-9B in 1956.

Work on updating the missile has gone on almost continually since. The early missiles could only operate in a tail aspect engagement while the current generation can engage a target from any angle. The second generation AIM-9 entered service in 1965 with the Navy and Air Force as the Navy AIM-9D and a semi-active radar seeker variant AIM-9C, while the Air Force developed the AIM-9E. The Army also used the missile as a surface-to-air system, the MIM-72 Chaparral.

These were followed by the Navy AIM-9G/H and the Air Force's AIM-9J/P. At this point the Navy and Air Force joined forces to develop a new generation of the Sidewinder. This missile, the AIM-9L, was superior to its predecessors both in its flight characteristics and in its storage and general operations. Production commenced in 1976 and this was followed in 1982 by the AIM-9M

AIM-120A
(AMRAAM)

Contractor:
Hughes Aircraft Company/
Raytheon Company

Status:
Operational

Guidance:
Inertial midcourse, with active
radar terminal homing

Dimensions:
Length 3.58 m (11 ft 9 in)
Body diameter 17.7 cm (7 in)
Span of tail control fins 63.5 cm
(2 ft 1 in)

Weights:
102 kg (335 lb)

Performance:
Cruising speed approx Mach 4

Aircraft types:
F-15, F-16

Below: These crewmen lend scale to the AIM-9 they carry

Notes:
The joint Air Force and Navy advanced medium-range air-to-air missile development program started in 1975. In 1979 Hughes and Raytheon entered a validation competition which was eventually won by Hughes in 1981. Hughes was asked to build 94 test missiles, with an option for 924 production missiles. The Air Force intends to acquire 17,000 missiles and the Navy has a need for 7,000.

The early development suffered a number of problems and in 1985 there was a complete program review, which provided for a two year extension to the development phase and the in-service date was moved from 1986 to 1989. The missile is designed as a replacement for the Sparrow and will arm the Navy's F-14 and F-18 and the Air Force's F-15 and F-16.

The active radar terminal seeker head, along with the track-while-scan radar on the launch aircraft, provides the capability to simultaneously track multiple targets, launch several missiles and then maneuver to avoid counterattack.

Work is continuing on a new advanced active radar terminal seeker and signal processor which could be used for an improved variant

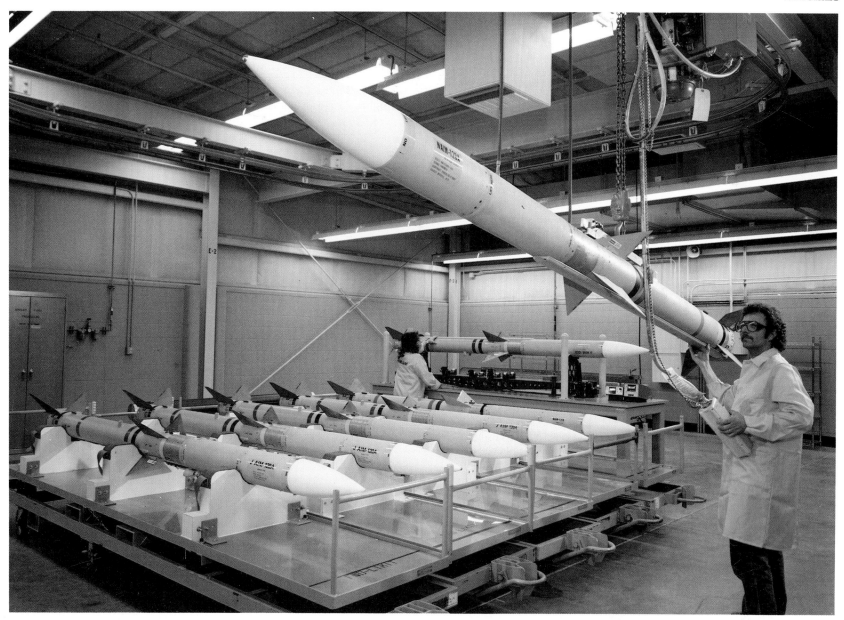

Above: AIM-120s being readied for delivery from the Hughes Aircraft plant

Below: An AIM-120 being attached to this F-15 at Eglin AFB

AIR-2A Genie

Contractor:
Douglas Aircraft Company

Status:
Retired

Powerplant:
Thiokol solid motor, 16,600 kg
(36,600 lb)

Guidance:
None, fins and gyroscope
stabilization

Warhead:
W-25, 1.5 kT nuclear

Dimensions:
Length 2.946 m (9 ft 8 in)
Body diameter 44.5 cm (1 ft 5.5 in)
excluding warhead
Wing span 1.016 m (3 ft 4 in)

Weights:
At launch 373 kg (822 lb)

Performance:
Speed Mach 3.3
Range 8–10 km (5–6.2 miles)

Aircraft types:
F-4D, F-15, F-89J, F-101B, F-106

Notes:
The world's most powerful air-to-air
missile, although not guided it flew a
near ballistic trajectory. Following
confirmation of tests on the nuclear
warhead at the Los Alamos Scien-
tific laboratory in 1955, Douglas
began work on this missile. It was
first fired from an F-89J in July 1957.
The missile was exploded by ground
control at a height of 4,572 m
(15,000 ft) above the test range at
Indian Springs, Nevada. During the
development stage of the program
the missile was codenamed Ding
Dong and then High Card. Designated MB-1 when it entered service,
it was redesignated AIR-2A in 1962.

In use, the aircraft's fire control
system tracked the enemy target, assigned the missile, then instructed
the pilot to arm the warhead. It then
fired the missile and pulled the aircraft into a tight turn to avoid the
target area, finally triggering the
missile when it was at the correct
range from the enemy aircraft. Production of the missile ended in 1962,
while the improved TU-289 motor
carried on in production until 1982

Right: This GBU-15 is slung from the
inboard wing pylon on an F-5E

GBU-15 and AGM-130A

Contractor:
Rockwell International Corporation

Status:
Operational

Guidance:
TV or imaging infrared seeker

Warhead:
Mk 84 bomb 900 kg (2,000 lb)
(unitary)

Dimensions:
Length 3.92 m (12 ft 10.5 in)
Body diameter 45 cm (1 ft 6 in)
Wing span 1.5 m (4 ft 11 in)

Weights:
1,187 kg (2,617 lb)

Performance:
Cruising speed subsonic

Aircraft types:
F-4, F-111

Notes:

Development began in 1974, with information gathered on the use of the earlier Pave Strike GBU-8 HOBO glide bombs that had been used in Vietnam. The GBU-15 is designed for use against heavily protected enemy defenses. It is made up of a cruciform-wing glide bomb with a guidance system strapped on the nose. The missile can be fired direct at a target where the missile seeker locks onto the target and flies a near line-of-sight path, or it can be controlled by the pilot of the launch aircraft who can make mid-course corrections to the flight path.

The missile is deployed on the F-4E and F-111 and has been tested on the F-15E and F-16D. The GBU-15(V)1/B, which is TV-guided, qualified for operational service in 1983, and the GBU-15(V)2/B imaging infrared version entered service in 1987. The last GBU-15s were delivered in 1987.

The AGM-130 was to have been a rocket powered variant, but the program was terminated in the amended FY 88–89 budget. Testing of the system has carried on using funds that had already been allocated and this project has provided much useful information

Inset: This F-106A launches an AIR-2

General Index